8/71

SYNOPSIS OF NEUROANATOMY

Synopsis of
Neuroanatomy

Howard A. Matzke, Ph.D.

PROFESSOR AND CHAIRMAN
DEPARTMENT OF ANATOMY
UNIVERSITY OF KANSAS MEDICAL CENTER

Floyd M. Foltz, Ph.D.

ASSOCIATE PROFESSOR
DEPARTMENT OF ANATOMY
UNIVERSITY OF KANSAS MEDICAL CENTER

OXFORD UNIVERSITY PRESS
NEW YORK   LONDON   TORONTO
1967

Third Printing, 1970

Copyright © 1967 by Oxford University Press, Inc.
Library of Congress Catalogue Card Number: 67-25463
Printed in the United States of America

Preface

The authors undertook the writing of this book because there is a need for a clear, concise, and yet comprehensive account of neuroanatomy. Concepts are emphasized and wherever possible, evolutionary development of each system is included. It was felt this would lead to a better understanding of the organization and dynamics of the human nervous system. Clinical applications are included only where they clearly aid in the understanding of the anatomy and physiology.

The authors wish to express their appreciation to Mr. P. A. Roberts, to Mr. Alan Cole, and to Dr. Nestor Bautista, who prepared the illustrations; to Mrs. Yvonne Roberts, Mrs. Grace Foltz, Mrs. Grace Matzke, and Mrs. Annette Richberg for typing various portions of this manuscript; to their many colleagues, graduate students, and medical students for reviewing and criticizing the work; and finally, to the staff of the Oxford University Press for their patience and many helpful suggestions throughout the preparation of this book.

Kansas City, Kansas　　　　　　　　　HOWARD A. MATZKE
1967　　　　　　　　　　　　　　　　FLOYD M. FOLTZ

Contents

SYNOPSIS OF NEUROANATOMY

1

Introduction

The nervous system of all but the simplest metazoans is built upon a foundation of the same basic elements. It exhibits the primary phenomena of irritability and conductivity. Distinct organizational modifications first appear in archaic vertebrate ancestry, and it is here that we first see the appearance of a dorsal tubular nervous system. Afferent (sensory) fibers arising from receptors in the periphery conduct information into the central nervous system, where it is modified and integrated and then directed to the appropriate effector apparatus (muscles and glands) by way of efferent (motor) fibers. The degree to which the response is modified and delayed is directly related to the complexity of the central nervous system.

The basic subdivisions of the central nervous system

are present in all vertebrates (Fig. 1); the caudal portion, i.e. the spinal cord, undergoes the least amount of change in phylogeny. The cephalic portion of the primitive neural tube differentiates into five primary brain vesicles. They are, from rostral to caudal: telencephalon, diencephalon, mesencephalon, metencephalon, and myelencephalon. From these vesicles develop the various adult structures of the brain. The telencephalon is divided into two halves called cerebral hemispheres. Each half contains a cavity, the lateral ventricle, which is an enlargement of the primitive central canal. The telencephalon gives rise to the cerebral cortex and basal ganglia, and the first cranial nerve (olfactory) is attached at this level.

The diencephalon is separated into two halves by a midline third ventricle, which communicates with the lateral ventricles by way of the interventricular foramen. In the adult the diencephalon is divided into the epithalamus, dorsal thalamus, subthalamus, and hypothalamus. The second cranial nerve (optic) enters the diencephalon.

Centrally the mesencephalon contains a constricted portion of the ventricular system, the cerebral aqueduct, which communicates with the third ventricle above. The third (oculomotor) and fourth (trochlear) cranial nerves are associated with the midbrain. The tectum, containing the corpora quadrigemina (inferior and superior colliculi), is dorsal to the aqueduct, whereas the tegmentum lies ventral.

The metencephalon differentiates into the cerebellum dorsally and the pons ventrally. The fifth (trigeminal), sixth (abducens), seventh (facial), and eighth (auditory) nerves attach to the pons.

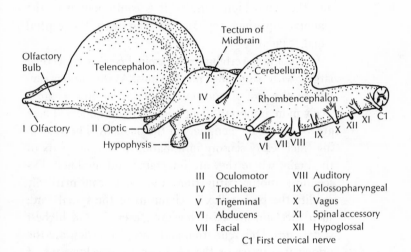

III	Oculomotor	VIII	Auditory
IV	Trochlear	IX	Glossopharyngeal
V	Trigeminal	X	Vagus
VI	Abducens	XI	Spinal accessory
VII	Facial	XII	Hypoglossal
	C1 First cervical nerve		

1. Generalized Vertebrate Brain

3

The myelencephalon develops into the medulla oblongata. The ninth (glossopharyngeal), tenth (vagus), eleventh (accessory), and twelfth (hypoglossal) cranial nerves are associated with the medulla. The fourth ventricle is related to the pons and medulla ventrally, and the cerebellum dorsally. It is continuous with the cerebral aqueduct cephalically, and with the central canal, caudally.

In the lower vertebrates the spinal cord is concerned largely with basic reflex mechanisms. As the various centers in the rostral portion, i.e. brain, become progressively more important, longitudinal tracts appear. These are located at the periphery of the neuraxis. The ascending tracts carry sensory information to various parts of the brain, where they are integrated and modified. Descending motor paths from the brain can markedly modify the basic reflex mechanisms of the spinal cord; such mechanisms exist, however, even in the highest vertebrates. Differentiation and encephalization are the principal features of the phylogenetic development of the central nervous system. Formation of specific nuclear groups and fiber paths appear progressively as the nervous system becomes more complex. Concurrently there is an increase in volume and importance of the cerebral cortex and its associated thalamic nuclei. This differentiation allows for a higher degree of discrimination in sensory perception and motor activity. Older diffuse pathways, however, still persist even in man, for it is generally true that once a structure appears in phylogeny it is never lost, although the size and function of these structures may be greatly modified by phylogenetically newer portions and by the animal's specialized adaptation to its habitat.

The increase in cortex and related subcortical areas, particularly the thalamus, results in a concomitant increase in the number of interneuronal connections. The ability of the animal to modify the response to a given set of afferent stimuli and to store information (memory) is proportional to the number and complexity of these connections. The capacities to plan and show concern for the future, to develop abstract reasoning, to use language and symbols, and to demonstrate an individual personality, are probably likewise functions of a highly developed cortex and thalamus. These faculties are usually reserved for man, but no doubt the rudimentary beginnings of some of them appear in certain subhuman forms.

2

Basic Elements of the Nervous System

The nerve cell (neuron) contains a cell body (perikaryon) and processes (axon and dendrites). Neurons vary in size and shape as well as in the number of processes they possess. Unipolar neurons (Fig. 2D) have but one process, which bifurcates. Unipolar neurons are found in the sensory ganglia associated with the dorsal roots of the spinal nerves and sensory ganglia of certain of the cranial nerves. Bipolar neurons (Fig. 2E), which have two processes, are located in the retina, olfactory membrane, and ganglion of the VIIIth (auditory) cranial nerve. Multipolar neurons (Fig. 2A) have three or more processes, one of which is an axon

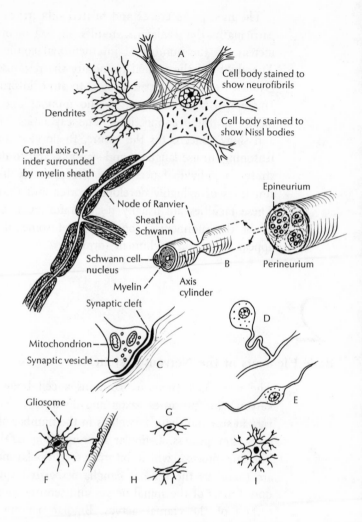

Dendrites

Cell body stained to show neurofibrils

Cell body stained to show Nissl bodies

Central axis cylinder surrounded by myelin sheath

Node of Ranvier

Sheath of Schwann

Schwann cell nucleus

Myelin

Axis cylinder

Epineurium

Perineurium

Synaptic cleft

Mitochondrion

Synaptic vesicle

Gliosome

2. Histology of Nervous Tissue   A. multipolar neuron
   B. peripheral nerve C. synapse D. unipolar neuron
   E. bipolar neuron F. fibrous astrocyte G. oligoden-
   drocyte H. microglia I. protoplasmic astrocyte

and the others dendrites, and are located in the central nervous system and autonomic ganglia.

The cell body contains a prominent nucleus (Fig. 2A) (usually centrally placed) with one or more nucleoli and a light staining chromatin net. The nucleolus contains ribonucleic acid (RNA) and the chromatin desoxyribonucleic acid (DNA). RNA is also distributed throughout the nucleoplasm. Scattered throughout the cytoplasm—except at the point of attachment of the axon, which is known as the axon hillock—are clumps of material called Nissl bodies (chromidial or tigroid substance). Nissl bodies, which also extend into the dendrites, vary from a fine powdery substance to regular block-like granules. They are readily demonstrated with basic aniline dyes. They are known to be composed of nucleoproteins and iron. Electron micrographs reveal Nissl bodies to be made up of a series of parallel membranes which may anastomose. The membranes contain RNA granules. The function of the Nissl bodies is not fully understood, but they probably play an important role in protein synthesis. When the neuron is injured the Nissl substance undergoes dissolution, a process known as chromatolysis. If recovery ensues the Nissl substance first reappears around the nuclear membrane. It is probably formed from material in the nucleus. Nissl substance is depleted during chronic stimulation of the cell.

Other intracellular structures found in all neurons are neurofibrils, which extend throughout the cytoplasm, dendrites, and axon. They are best demonstrated by metallic impregnation techniques, e.g. silver. Early investigators believed that they were concerned with the conduction of the nerve impulse, but conduction is now known to be a surface phenomenon. They may be concerned with metabolism or the transport of nutrient.

Mitochondria are found throughout the cytoplasm, dendrites, and axon and are particularly concentrated at the terminal ends of nerve fibers. Their structure and function are similar to those found in other cell types. They are spherical or elongated and are composed of unit membranes formed of phospholipids combined with protein. Mitochondria are double membranous structures with the inner layer thrown into folds called cristae. Associated with the outer aspects of the inner membrane are the enzymes for the tricarboxylic acid cycle. On the inner aspect are the enzymes for the cytochrome electron transfer system. They are, therefore, the site for aerobic respiration in the cell. Current research indicates that within the matrix of mitochondria there may be other enzyme systems.

A Golgi apparatus is found within the nerve cell cytoplasm. This is a fine reticular network of unit membranes in the form of flattened sacs, and large and small vesicles. It is known that in gland cells they play a role in secretion and may have a similar function in neurosecretion. They are very sensitive to nerve cell injury, undergoing fragmentation and dissolution before the Nissl substance.

Other cytoplasmic inclusions found in nerve cells are vacuoles, fatty substances, melanin pigment (confined to specific cells), and lipochrome pigment. The last increases with age.

A neuron may have one dendrite or many. The dendrite is usually short but branches profusely and at any angle. It is attached to the cell body by a broad base but tapers in diameter rapidly. Dendrites contain Nissl substance and mitochondria. They conduct toward the cell body, and thus are in synaptic relation with the terminal ends of a large number of axons.

In contrast to the dendrite the axon is usually long and does not taper. There is only one to a cell. The axon is devoid of Nissl substance but does contain mitochondria and many neurofibrils. Branches of the axon are few in number except at the terminal end. Those that come off in the course of the fiber are called collaterals. They arise at right angles at the nodes of Ranvier. The axon conducts the impulse away from the cell body.

The axon may have one or two coverings: myelin and sheath of Schwann (Fig. 2B). The actual extension of the cell body is known as the axis cylinder, and surrounding this may be a lipoid material, myelin, which appears in concentric lamellae. In the peripheral nervous system, and also centrally, the myelin is broken into segments. The nodes of Ranvier are the points at which the axis cylinder is devoid of myelin. Outside the myelin sheath in the peripheral nervous system is found a single cell layered membrane, the sheath of Schwann. The Schwann cell constains a scanty amount of cytoplasm but a prominent nucleus. One sheath cell occupies one internodal space. Surrounding peripheral nerve fibers is a thin tubular membrane known as the neurilemma which comes in contact with the axis cylinder at the nodes and constitutes the outer membrane of the Schwann cell. It is believed that the sheath forms the myelin as it circumnavigates the axis cylinder by

9

laying down concentric lamellae, formed largely from plasma membranes of the Schwann cell. In the central nervous system this function is subserved by specialized cells called oligodendrocytes. At the terminal end of the axon the sheaths are lost and the fiber branches at all angles forming terminal naked fibers called telodendria.

The synapse (Fig. 2C) is the junction between the terminal ends of an axon of one neuron and the dendrites or cell body of another. Synaptic endings have also been described in relation to the naked proximal end of the axon. Protoplasmic continuity does not exist at the synapse but there is contiguity. Electron microscopists have described a synaptic cleft between the thickened presynaptic and subsynaptic membranes of about 200 Å.

Synaptic terminals may take on various forms. A common form is a ball-like ending known as a bouton. Other types are basket endings, knobs, spines, and rings. The presynaptic endings contain mitochondria and synaptic vesicles. The latter contains the chemical mediator which may be released into the synaptic cleft upon arrival of an impulse. The synapse is polarized; conduction is from the axon of one neuron to the dendrites or cell body of another.

Other elements found within the central nervous system are the neuroglia, comprised of astrocytes, oligodendrocytes, and microglia. Astrocytes, arising from ectoderm, are divided into two types, fibrous and protoplasmic. Both types are found in gray and white matter though the fibrous type is more numerous in the white matter and the protoplasmic type in the gray. The fibrous astrocytes (Fig. 2F) contain numerous fibrous processes which rarely branch. The cell body contains an oval nucleus with little chromatin. There is also very little cytoplasm. The processes contain granules called gliosomes. Some of the processes have expansions around blood vessels known as perivascular end feet. The fibers also form a network around the nerve cells. Fibrous astrocytes are found in large numbers at the surface of the central nervous system, where, with the pia mater, they form the pial-glial membrane. Protoplasmic astrocytes (Fig. 2I) contain numerous thick processes which branch profusely. The processes have gliosomes and perivascular end feet. The nucleus has the same appearance as the fibrous astrocytes, but the cell body contains more cytoplasm.

Oligodendrocytes (Fig. 2G), which are also derived from ectoderm, are smaller than astrocytes and are found in both gray and white matter. In the gray matter they frequently are found as satellites to neurons. In the white matter they are located along the course of the nerve fibers. Oligodendrocytes have a few slender processes with few branches. There are no perivascular end feet, but gliosomes are present. The nucleus stains darker than in astrocytes and the cytoplasm is scanty.

Microglia (Fig. 2H) are of mesodermal origin. They are probably part of the reticulo-endothelial system since they revert to phagocytes following injury to the nervous system. The cells are very small and have delicate tortuous processes. They are found in both gray and white matter, and the cell body varies considerably in shape.

The neuroglia have a number of functions and have long been recognized as supportive. Because of their close relation to the neurons and blood vessels it is felt that they constitute the blood brain barrier. They play an important role in the transport of materials between the blood and nerve cell. Recently contacts have been described between glia and nerve cells and glia and glia, and it has been speculated that glia may be conductive since the contacts might be a mechanism for electrotonic spread of potentials. Finally, as stated above, oligodendrocytes play an important role in the formation of myelin in the central nervous system.

Peripheral nerves contain a variable number of nerve fibers. Usually within each nerve the fibers are organized into several bundles known as fascicles (Fig. 2B). Each fascicle is surrounded by a selectively permeable cellular membrane called the perilemma or perineural epithelium. Within each fascicle are myelinated and nonmyelinated fibers supported by a delicate connective tissue known as the endoneurium. Immediately outside the perilemma is the perineurium, which is a dense connective tissue composed of elastic and collagenous fibers and containing numerous blood vessels and lymphatics. All the fascicles are bound together into one nerve trunk by the epineurium, which is a loose connective tissue containing collagenous and elastic fibers, fat, and blood vessels. It blends in with the connective tissue of the surrounding structures. The endoneurium, perineurium, and epineurium are derived from the mesoderm.

A single nerve fiber may be afferent or efferent and be concerned with either the soma or viscera. This results in four functional components of peripheral nerves. General somatic afferent (GSA) fibers convey afferent impulses from the general soma such as the skin, bone, skeletal muscle, joints, ligaments, tendons, etc. General visceral afferent (GVA) fibers arise from receptors in the viscera, including blood vessels. General somatic efferent (GSE) fibers innervate skeletal muscles derived from myotomes. General visceral efferent (GVE) fibers belong to the autonomic nervous system and supply smooth and cardiac muscles and glands.

Generally, all spinal nerves contain these components. In the cranial nerves there may be three additional components due to the presence of special sense organs and skeletal muscle derived from branchial arches. Nerve fibers supplying the branchial muscles are referred to as special visceral efferent (SVE). Special visceral afferent (SVA) fibers arise from the chemical receptors of taste and smell, whereas the special somatic afferent (SSA) component is associated with the special sense of sight and receptors in the inner ear.

No cranial nerve has all seven components. The following are the components of each of the cranial nerves:

I	Olfactory	SVA
II	Optic	SSA
III	Oculomotor	GSE, GVE
IV	Trochlear	GSE
V	Trigeminal	GSA, SVE
VI	Abducens	GSE
VII	Facial	SVE, SVA, GVE, GVA, GSA
VIII	Auditory	SSA
IX	Glossopharyngeal	SVE, SVA, GVE, GVA, GSA
X	Vagus	SVE, SVA, GVE, GVA, GSA
XI	Spinal accessory	SVE
XII	Hypoglossal	GSE

In addition, the oculomotor, trochlear, abducens, and hypoglossal may contain proprioceptive fibers which are GSA.

Within the central nervous system each functional component is usually represented by a column of cells which may or may not be discontinuous throughout the neuraxis. Thus, as a peripheral nerve approaches the central nervous system its individual functional components separate out and terminate in (afferent) or arise from (efferent) a nucleus belonging to the column related to its function.

3

Basic Neural Mechanisms

In the spinal cord the gray matter which contains cell bodies is arranged in a central H-shaped mass (Fig. 3C). Peripheral to this is the white matter, made up largely of myelinated fibers. The gray matter is composed of aggregates of cell bodies known as nuclei. The neurons making up a nucleus generally have similar connections and functions. Entering the spinal cord at the apex of the dorsal horn of the gray matter is the dorsal root of the spinal nerve. The cell bodies of these fibers are unipolar and are located in the dorsal root ganglion. A ganglion is an aggregate of cell bodies outside the central nervous system. The ventral root exists from the base of the ventral horn of the gray matter. The cell bodies of these fibers are multipolar and located in the ventral horn.

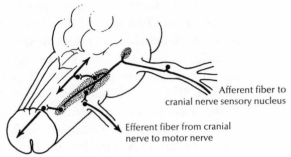

Afferent fiber to
cranial nerve sensory nucleus

Efferent fiber from cranial
nerve to motor nerve

A. BRAIN STEM REFLEX PATHWAYS

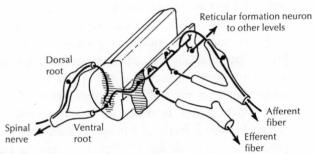

Reticular formation neuron
to other levels

Dorsal
root

Afferent
fiber

Spinal
nerve

Ventral
root

Efferent
fiber

B. SPINAL CORD REFLEX PATHWAYS

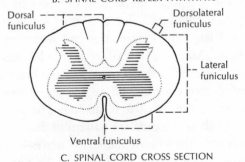

Dorsal
funiculus

Dorsolateral
funiculus

Lateral
funiculus

Ventral funiculus

C. SPINAL CORD CROSS SECTION

3. Reflex Pathways

The white matter is divided into three masses of fibers known as funiculi. The dorsal funiculus is located between the dorsal midline and dorsal root, the lateral funiculus between the dorsal and ventral roots, and the ventral funiculus between the ventral root and ventral midline. Within each funiculus are found bundles of fibers called fasciculi or tracts. The fibers within a fasciculus usually have a common origin, termination, and function. They may be either ascending or descending.

The orderly arrangement of gray and white matter remains constant throughout the spinal cord, varying only in relative mass. The volume of gray matter reflects the size of the spinal nerve associated with that level. Thus its size is markedly increased at the cervical and lumbosacral segments of the spinal cord for the innervation of upper and lower extremities respectively. The white matter increases in absolute mass from caudal to rostral levels of the spinal cord due to the progressive accumulation of fibers in ascending fasciculi and a gradual diminution of fibers in descending tracts. In the brain, due to factors which will be discussed later, the gray matter and white matter intermingle. More or less discrete nuclei and fasciculi appear usually at the periphery of the brain stem. The central core contains diffuse tracts and nuclei and is known as the reticular formation. The cranial nerves do not show the constant pattern of dorsal and ventral roots as is the case of the spinal nerves—they may be either purely sensory or motor. If the nerve is mixed the fibers enter and leave the brain stem in the same root. Centrally, the nuclei associated with cranial nerves are arranged in functional columns; the fibers separate centrally and arise or terminate in the appropriate column.

The reflex arc usually consists of a receptor, afferent neuron, intercalated neuron (association or internuncial), efferent neuron, and effector. In a few instances (the stretch or myotatic reflex) the intercalated neuron may be absent. The receptors vary considerably in complexity from naked nerve endings to complicated receptor organs like the retina and organ of Corti. The receptor responding to an adequate stimulus sets up an impulse in the afferent neuron whose cell body is located in the dorsal root ganglion or one of the ganglia of the cranial nerves. The afferent neuron conveys the impulse centrally via the dorsal root of the spinal nerve or one of the cranial nerves. Upon entering the spinal cord (Fig. 3B) the fibers of the dorsal root bifurcate into ascending and descending limbs. These fibers course up and down a variable number of segments and terminate in synaptic relationship with neurons within the dorsal and intermediate gray matter. These intercalated neurons will either synapse directly or indirectly (by way of other intercalated neurons) with efferent neurons of the ventral horn. The efferent neuron whose cell body is located in the ventral horn will exit by way of the ventral root or one of the cranial nerves, ending in relation to an effector, which may be either a muscle or gland.

The course and termination of the intercalated neuron determine the pattern of the reflex response. The intercalated neuron may ascend or descend a number of segments, resulting in an intersegmental reflex. If the intercalated neuron is confined to the same segment into which the afferent fiber enters, the result will be an intrasegmental reflex. The intercalated neuron may cross to the opposite side, resulting in a crossed or contralateral reflex. In this case the intercalated neuron is referred to as commissural. Many of the axons of the intercalated neuron ascend and descend for a considerable distance in a band of fibers surrounding the gray matter. This group of fibers is referred to as the fasciculus proprius or fasciculus spinospinalis. Other spinal reflex tracts are the septomarginal fasciculus, located in the dorsal funiculus adjacent to the median sulcus, and the fasciculus interfascicularis, or comma bundle, located in relationship to the intermediate septum of the dorsal funiculus. These tracts contain ascending and descending limbs of the dorsal root fibers. They ultimately terminate on internuncial neurons.

Afferent fibers of cranial nerves terminate in specific nuclei (Fig. 3A). Neurons within these nuclei may constitute intercalated neurons of reflex arcs. These fibers may pass directly to motor nuclei, ascend or descend in specific fasciculi, or enter the reticular formation. The last is continuous with the fasciculus proprius of the spinal cord. Over this pathway may be mediated many of the reflexes involving spinal and cranial nerves.

Before proceeding to a detailed discussion of specific sensory pathways it may be profitable to first point out those features common to all such systems (Fig. 4). The exceptions to the general pattern presented will be pointed out as the specific pathways are discussed. The cell body of the primary neuron is located in a ganglion which is outside the central nervous system. The peripheral process of the neuron is incorporated in a spinal or cranial nerve and terminates in relation to a receptor. The receptors respond to various stimuli and

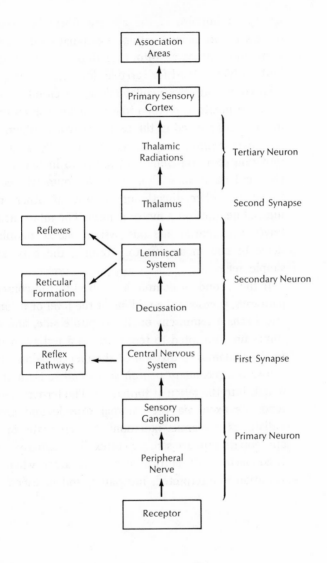

4. General Principles of Sensory Pathways

set up an impulse in the afferent fiber. The central process of the neuron enters the spinal cord or brain stem and bifurcates into ascending and descending limbs, which extend for variable distances. Throughout their course numerous collaterals are given off. Sensory fibers terminate in relation to a secondary neuron found in a nucleus located in the central nervous system. The secondary neuron may project cephalically as a continuation of a conscious pathway or to higher integrative centers. It may also, as an internuncial neuron, terminate either directly or by way of other internuncial neurons on a motor neuron. The motor neuron leaves the central nervous system via a peripheral nerve to end in an effector, forming the basis for a simple reflex arc.

If the secondary neuron is involved in the conscious pathways, it crosses the midline at the level of its origin and forms a lemniscus on the opposite side, and continues uninterrupted to terminate on a tertiary neuron in the thalamus, a division of the diencephalon. In its course the secondary neuron sends collaterals and terminals into the reticular formation. The tertiary neuron sends its axon via the internal capsule and corona radiata as thalamic radiations to terminate in the appropriate primary sensory cortex. The primary cortex is connected with cortical association areas, where the sensation is interpreted, integrated, and modified.

4

Pain, Temperature, and Tactile Pathways

The general features of sensory systems have been covered, and now the pain, temperature, and tactile pathways will be described. The receptors for these pathways are naked nerve endings and simple encapsulated organs (Fig. 5). In the case of pain a poorly myelinated or non-myelinated fiber branches profusely and ends as a naked terminal among the epithelial cells of the skin and viscera, in subcutaneous tissue, and in the walls of blood vessels. Some fibers terminate in a cup-like expansion in relation to a specialized epithelial cell. These are thought to be tactile receptors (Merkel's tactile disc), which respond to light touch. Other tactile receptors are the peritrichial endings, which are naked fibers forming a basket-like arrangement around the hair follicles. Simple encapsulated endings, such as the end bulbs of Krause, serve as temperature receptors. They are composed of a simple capsule of connective tissue surrounding a central core containing a gelatinous matrix. The receptor is round and contains a nerve fiber which loses its sheaths upon entering the gelatinous core, branches profusely, and ends in knob-like expansions.

The fibers of the peripheral nerves, which convey impulses originating in the receptors cited above, are poorly myelinated or non-myelinated. Their cell bodies are small, unipolar, and are located in the cerebrospinal ganglia. In the spinal nerves the central processes of

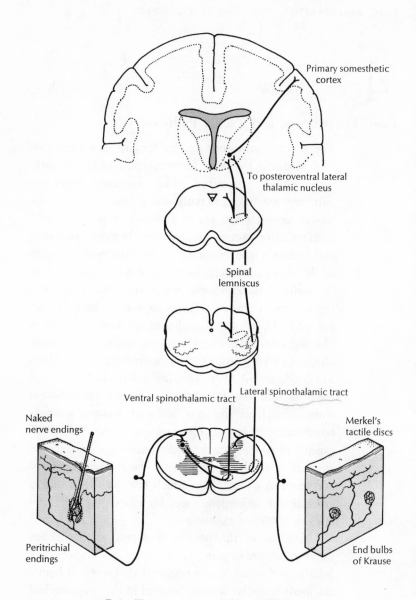

Primary somesthetic cortex

To posteroventral lateral thalamic nucleus

Spinal lemniscus

Ventral spinothalamic tract

Lateral spinothalamic tract

Naked nerve endings

Peritrichial endings

Merkel's tactile discs

End bulbs of Krause

5. Pain, Temperature, and Tactile Pathways

these cells separate from other fibers of the dorsal root to make up its lateral division, and upon entering the spinal cord they bifurcate and ascend or descend in the dorsolateral fasciculus (zone of Lissauer) for only a few segments. The fibers and the numerous collaterals terminate in the substantia gelatinosa and dorsal funicular gray, which are nuclear groups at the apex of the dorsal horn. Secondary fibers arising from these nuclei make connections with various nuclear groups within the spinal cord for the purpose of mediating reflexes, as outlined in Chapter 3.

Other fibers arising from cells in the dorsal gray cross the midline in the ventral white commissure and ascend in the lateral and ventral funiculi, where they form the lateral and ventral spinothalamic and spinotectal tracts. The lateral spinothalamic tract projects impulses of pain and temperature to higher centers. In the cord it is located in the ventrolateral portion of the lateral funiculus. Lamination occurs in that the first fibers entering the tract and representing sacral levels are the most lateral. Fibers entering at successively higher levels assume a more medial position. Throughout the medulla and pons the tract maintains a lateral position. It then migrates dorsally in the midbrain, and upon reaching diencephalic levels turns laterally to terminate in the posteroventral lateral nucleus of the thalamus. Throughout its course the lateral spinothalamic tract sends numerous collaterals into the intermediate. and ventral gray of the cord and reticular formation of the brain stem.

The thalamus is the lowest level of sensory appreciation. There is, however, poor localization in that only the pleasantness or unpleasantness of a sensation is realized. Discrimination is a function of the cortex. Fibers from the posteroventral lateral nucleus of the thalamus project as general thalamic radiations through the internal capsule and corona radiata to terminate in the postcentral gyrus, which constitutes the primary somesthetic cortex. The primary cortex has extensive connections with association areas where the sensation is interpreted and integrated with other incoming information.

The ventral spinothalamic tract is probably concerned with projecting tactile, i.e. light touch, impulses to higher centers. In the spinal cord it ascends in the periphery of the ventral funiculus. Its position in the brain stem is not clear. It may course with the lateral spinothalamic tract or in a more medial position; localization within the tract has not been determined. It terminates in the posteroventral lateral nucleus of the thalamus. Subsequent connections are the same as for pain and temperature.

The spinotectal tract conveys tactile and pain impulses to the midbrain tectum. It ascends ventral to or intermingled with the fibers of the lateral spinothalamic tract and, upon reaching the upper pons, courses dorsally and terminates in the tectum. The tectum, particularly in lower forms, is an important center for motor integration. It receives sensory impulses from a variety of sources, including visual and auditory. Although some of its functions have been superseded by higher centers, it still maintains the connections it established early in phylogeny.

A spinothalamic system exists only in mammals. This is related to the appearance of sensory areas in the neocortex. The lowest vertebrates, however, show the beginnings of this system. In primitive jawless verte-brates (cyclostomes) a system of fibers can be traced across the midline in the cord and followed as high as the brain-stem reticular formation, which in these forms constitutes the most important motor center of integration. In its course collaterals are given off to the spinal cord gray. With the development of the tectum (fish, amphibians, reptiles) as an important motor center, the fibers of this system reach midbrain levels but still maintain connections with cord and reticular formation. Finally, in mammals a neocortex appears and a true spinothalamic system is present. Neverthe-less, all the connections previously established are maintained.

A number of clinical conditions demonstrate the anatomy of the pain and temperature pathway. In cases of intractable pain the lateral spinothalamic tract may be sectioned in the spinal cord, the operation of cordotomy. The inability to perceive pain and detect temperature change is on the opposite side of the body, and will extend as high as a few segments below the level of the section. This is due to the fact that when the dorsal root fibers enter they ascend and descend for a few segments. If the tract is involved in a lesion in the brain stem there is a complete loss of sense of pain and temperature change on the opposite side of the body. A degenerative condition known as syringo-myelia begins around the central canal, usually in the cervical enlargement, with interruption of the ventral white commissure which conveys pain and temperature fibers from the dorsal horn across the midline. The first sign is a bilateral segmental loss of sense of pain and temperature change in the upper extremities.

5

Proprioception, Tactile Discrimination, and Stereognosis

This system includes the sense of position and movement (proprioception), two-point discrimination, vibratory sense, and stereognosis (three-dimensional sense). The receptors for this system are much more complicated than for pain and temperature. The system contains several types of encapsulated organs (Meissner's, Golgi-Mazzoni, and Pacinian corpuscles) which vary in size, shape, and manner of fiber termination (Fig. 6). In each case a myelinated fiber loses its myelin upon entering the core of the receptor. The neurilemma blends with the connective tissue capsule.

Meissner's corpuscle is elongated and contains a thin connective-tissue capsule. The nerve fiber, upon entering the gelatinous core, spirals and branches considerably. The fibers terminate as swellings in relation to flattened cells. The Golgi-Mazzoni corpuscle is small and spherical. The capsule is slightly thicker than Meissner's, the nerve fiber is less coiled, and branching is sparse. The Pacinian corpuscle is the largest of the group, measuring from 1–4 mm. in length. It is oval in shape with a very heavy capsule. The fiber continues to the distal end of the core, ends in a knob, and may give off a few short branches en route. Nerve fibers have been observed to pass through a corpuscle to enter another. The Pacinian corpuscles, which are located in the dermis, in the superficial fascia, in the proximity of blood vessels, and in the viscera, are touch and pressure receptors.

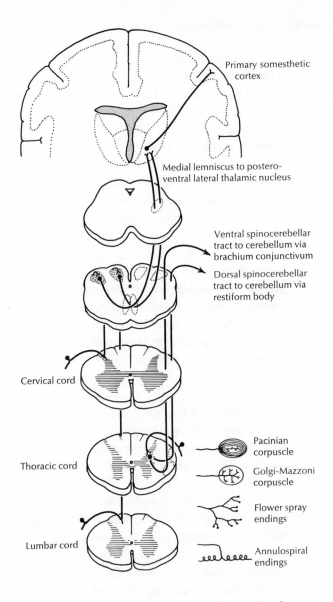

Primary somesthetic cortex

Medial lemniscus to postero-ventral lateral thalamic nucleus

Ventral spinocerebellar tract to cerebellum via brachium conjunctivum

Dorsal spinocerebellar tract to cerebellum via restiform body

Cervical cord

Thoracic cord

Pacinian corpuscle

Golgi-Mazzoni corpuscle

Flower spray endings

Lumbar cord

Annulospiral endings

6. Proprioception and Two-Point Discrimination Pathways

Proprioceptors are located in muscles and tendons. The neuromuscular endings are composed of a varying number of modified muscle fibers (intrafusal fibers) surrounded by a thin connective-tissue capsule. The polar ends of the intrafusal fiber contain typical skeletal muscle striations, but as the equatorial region is reached these are lost. The equatorial portion of the fiber is enlarged and contains numerous nuclei. This is referred to as the nuclear bag. The myotubes or polar regions, containing chains of nuclei, are located at either end of the nuclear bag. A large afferent myelinated fiber loses its myelin and neurilemma as it passes through the capsule. The fiber ends by spiraling around the nuclear bag region and is called an annulospiral ending. Smaller myelinated fibers enter the ends of the neuromuscular receptor and terminate on the myotube portion of the intrafusal fiber. These are known as flower spray endings. Each polar region receives a motor fiber called the gamma efferent. The flower spray endings are stimulated by stretch as well as contraction of the intrafusal fiber brought about by stimulation of the gamma efferent. Some investigators feel the annulospiral endings are intramuscular pressure receptors stimulated by the contraction of the muscle.

The neurotendinous ending is a tension receptor. A group of tendon fibers is surrounded by a capsule. The nerve fiber, which loses its myelin and neurilemma upon penetrating the capsule, branches profusely and terminates among the tendon fibers.

All spinal nerves and many of the cranial nerves carry fibers which convey proprioceptive impulses. The fibers are relatively large and well myelinated and conduct at a rapid rate. The cell bodies, located in the dorsal root ganglia or the ganglia of cranial nerves, are large as compared with those for pain. The fibers of the spinal nerves conveying the impulses enter the spinal cord by way of the medial division of the dorsal root. They enter the dorsal funiculus where they bifurcate into ascending and descending limbs. Some of these fibers may enter one of the reflex pathways located in the dorsal funiculus (fasciculus interfascicularis or septomarginal fasciculus) and eventually effect a reflex connection with neurons in the dorsal and intermediate gray or, in the case of the myotatic reflex, directly on the ventral horn cell.

A lamination occurs in the dorsal funiculus in that the fibers entering at the lowest level (sacral fibers) assume a position adjacent to the dorsomedial septum. As more and more fibers enter, they take up a more lateral position. The cervical fibers are therefore the most lateral of the group. Upon attaining the midthoracic region a septum begins to appear in the dorsal funiculus. This, the dorsal intermediate septum, separates the dorsal funiculus into two fasciculi. The medial group of fibers is referred to as the fasciculus gracilis. It contains fibers which have entered via the sacral, lumbar, and lower thoracic nerves. The lateral group is called the fasciculus cuneatus. Fibers which make up this fasciculus enter at upper thoracic and cervical levels. The fibers of these two fasciculi terminate in corresponding nuclei in the medulla, the nucleus gracilis and the nucleus cuneatus (dorsal column nuclei). This constitutes the first synapse in the pathway to the cerebral cortex.

Secondary fibers arising from these nuclei cross the

midline in a sweeping arc, and are referred to as internal arcuate fibers. Upon attaining the opposite side they ascend adjacent to the midline in a tract called the medial lemniscus. Throughout the medulla the medial lemniscus is situated adjacent to the midline, and upon reaching the pons it migrates laterally, assuming the shape of a horizontal band. In the upper portion of the pons it begins to pass dorsolaterally and continues in this position into the midbrain. When the thalamus is reached it passes into the posteroventral lateral nucleus, where the fibers terminate. This constitutes the second synapse in this pathway. Tertiary fibers arise from this nucleus and ascend via the internal capsule and corona radiata to terminate in the cortex of the postcentral gyrus. This area constitutes the primary somesthetic cortex. It has extensive connections with adjacent association cortex.

Some of the primary fibers coursing in the dorsal funiculus terminate in the nucleus dorsalis (Clarke's column) found at the base of the dorsal horn in the thoracic region. The axons of the cells in this nucleus ascend as the dorsal spinocerebellar tract in the dorsolateral portion of the lateral funiculus of the same side. They continue into the medulla, where they enter the restiform body (inferior cerebellar peduncle), then pass by way of this peduncle to terminate in the vermis portion of the cerebellar cortex. Other scattered cells in the dorsal horn give rise to the ventral spinocerebellar tract. The fibers which terminate among these scattered cells are likewise primary fibers from the dorsal funiculus. The ventral spinocerebellar tract probably contains some crossed fibers. This tract ascends peripheral to the lateral spinothalamic tract through the cord, medulla, and pons. Upon reaching the upper levels of the pons, it enters the brachium conjunctivum (superior cerebellar peduncle), and then enters the cerebellum to terminate in the cortex of the vermis. Lateral to the nucleus cuneatus in the medulla is located a mass of neurons whose structure is similar to the nucleus dorsalis in the cord. This nucleus is referred to as the external (lateral or accessory) cuneate nucleus. Many of the primary fibers of the fasciculus cuneatus terminate in this nucleus. Secondary neurons arising from this nucleus enter the adjacent restiform body and also terminate in the vermis of the cerebellum. These are referred to as direct (dorsal) arcuate fibers. These three tracts, dorsal spinocerebellar tract, ventral spinocerebellar tract, and direct arcuate fibers, constitute important pathways for proprioception from the skeletal muscles of the trunk to the cerebellum. The functional significance of this will be discussed in a later section.

Encapsulated receptors resembling those found in this system first appear in amphibians. A cortical pathway for them is present only in mammals. Again this is related to the development of the neocortex and the resulting increase in sensory discrimination. Dorsal column nuclei can be recognized in reptiles and birds. They project, however, only to the reticular formation and tectum. A true medial lemniscus reaching the thalamus is a mammalian acquisition. It may be expected that since the dorsal column nuclei of reptiles and birds project to the reticular formation and tectum, the medial lemniscus of mammals would give off collaterals to these areas. Very few, however, have been described. It may be that proprioception and tactile modalities reach these levels by direct spinoreticular and spinotectal tracts.

Tabes dorsalis and pernicious anemia attack the dorsal funiculus, destroying the component fibers. Any interruption of the proprioceptive pathway will be manifested by a lack of knowledge of the position of the limbs, spatial discrimination, loss of vibratory sense, etc. The patient has to watch his feet to walk since he is not aware of their position by way of proprioception. He also loses the sense of two-point discrimination and some vibratory sensibility. Lesions which interrupt the medial lemniscus may result in the same set of symptoms. Since the medial lemniscus is adjacent to many other important pathways, however, other symptoms referable to those pathways will also be present. It is to be remembered that a unilateral lesion of the dorsal funiculus will give rise to homolateral symptoms, whereas a unilateral lesion of the medial lemniscus will result in contralateral deficits.

Trigeminal Pathways

The trigeminal nerve is the principal somesthetic nerve of the head. It supplies all of the skin anterior to a line drawn from the crown through the ear to a point under the mandible. In addition it supplies a considerable area of the cranial meninges and the mucous membrane of the oral and nasal cavities, including the teeth. The receptors associated with it are the same as those discussed in the preceding chapters. The cell bodies of these afferent fibers are identical to those found in the dorsal root ganglia. They are located in the trigeminal (semilunar or Gasserian) ganglion (Fig. 7). The peripheral processes of these ganglion cells are distributed via the three divisions of the nerve. The central processes gather in a single bundle called the sensory root of the trigeminal nerve. This root courses through the middle of the brachium pontis. Its fibers run at near right angles to those of the brachium. Upon reaching the medial portion of the brachium pontis, the sensory root bifurcates into ascending and descending divisions. Approximately half of the constituent fibers descend. Most of the remainder bifurcate into ascending and descending divisions. A few ascend only. The descending root is concerned primarily with pain, temperature, and light touch, while the ascending division serves proprioception, two-point discrimination, and light touch. The descending fibers continue through the lateral portion of the tegmentum of the pons, and into the lateral aspect of the medulla, and finally blend with the fibers of the zone of Lissauer in the upper cervical segments of the cord. Through the pons the descending root is covered laterally by the brachium pontis. In the upper half of the medulla it is covered by the restiform body. It reaches the surface in the lower medulla and upper cervical cord. Throughout the course of the descending root a nucleus, the descending nucleus of V, is located medial to the root. Fibers of the descending root terminate in all levels of the nucleus. Three subdivisions of the descending nucleus of V can be recognized. The subnucleus caudalis extends from the level of the caudal third of the

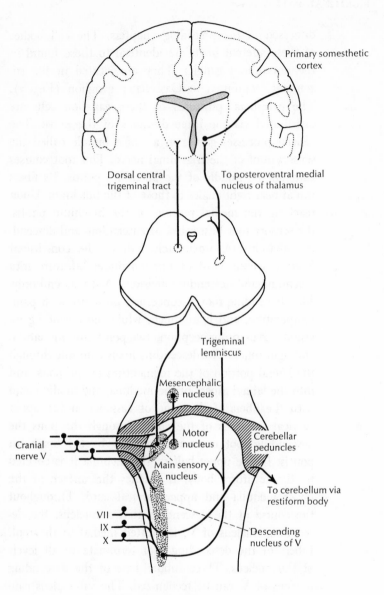

Primary somesthetic cortex

Dorsal central trigeminal tract

To posteroventral medial nucleus of thalamus

Trigeminal lemniscus

Mesencephalic nucleus

Motor nucleus

Cranial nerve V

Cerebellar peduncles

Main sensory nucleus

To cerebellum via restiform body

VII
IX
X

Descending nucleus of V

7. Trigeminal Pathways

inferior olive to C 3 or 4. It resembles in all respects the gray matter at the apex of the dorsal horn with which it is continuous. The subnucleus interpolaris is found at the level of the middle third of the inferior olive, and the subnucleus rostralis extends from this point to the level of entrance of the trigeminal nerve. The small fibers of the trigeminal nerve descend only, terminate in the subnucleus caudalis, and are concerned with pain and temperature. Those fibers which bifurcate terminate at all levels of the descending nucleus as well as in the main sensory nucleus which is associated with the ascending root, and are thought to be for light touch or poorly localized tactile sensibility. The larger fibers which ascend only terminate in the main sensory nucleus and are related to discriminatory touch.

Secondary fibers arise from all levels of the descending nucleus, cross the midline, and ascend in a diffuse tract in the lateral portion of the medulla. This tract is called the trigeminal lemniscus (ventral division of the trigeminal lemniscus, ventral central trigeminal tract). Throughout its course in the medulla and pons, numerous collaterals and terminals enter the reticular formation. In the upper pons the fibers intermingle with those of the medial lemniscus and accompany this tract into the thalamus. In the midbrain, fibers are given off to the tectum and tegmentum. The trigeminal lemniscus terminates in the posteroventral medial nucleus of the thalamus. Tertiary fibers from this nucleus project by way of the internal capsule and corona radiata to terminate in the postcentral gyrus. As in the case of the other systems, this gyrus has numerous connections with association areas.

The ascending root of the trigeminal nerve is short. Cells which intermingle with, and are located lateral to it, constitute the main sensory nucleus. The ascending root, whose fibers are for tactile discrimination, terminates in the main sensory nucleus. Secondary fibers from this nucleus ascend to the thalamus as the dorsal central trigeminal tract (dorsal division of the trigeminal lemniscus). Some fibers join the opposite trigeminal lemniscus. Others ascend on the same and opposite sides ventral to the central gray of the midbrain. They terminate in the posteroventral medial nucleus and subsequent connections with the cortex are the same as those described previously.

Proprioceptive fibers from the muscles of mastication also course with the trigeminal nerve. These fibers enter with the motor division, course adjacent to the motor and main sensory nuclei, and ascend in a bundle (mesencephalic root of V) to their cells of origin adjacent to the central gray of the midbrain. This is known as the mesencephalic nucleus of V. Its cells are unipolar, and their single processes make up the mesencephalic tract. As the fibers pass the motor nucleus, collaterals, which are the same as the central processes of unipolar ganglion cells, are given off to this nucleus. This is the basis for a myotatic reflex involving the muscles of mastication. Other collaterals may enter the main sensory nucleus, and by this connection proprioception may reach higher conscious levels.

The main sensory and descending nuclei also send numerous fibers into the reticular formation bilaterally. This is in part a reflex path but, as will be pointed out later, it is related to other important functions of the reticular formation. The trigeminal nuclei also project to both sides of the cerebellum by way of the restiform body.

The facial, glossopharyngeal, and vagus nerves each has a general somatic afferent component. These fibers are distributed to the skin of the pinna and external auditory meatus of the external ear. In addition the vagus innervates a portion of the cranial meninges. The cell bodies of these fibers are unipolar and are located in the geniculate ganglion of VII, the superior ganglion of IX, and the jugular ganglion of X. The central processes of these cells enter the descending root of the trigeminal nerve and terminate in the descending nucleus. Subsequent connections are the same as those described above. Thus all the general somatic afferents of cranial nerves terminate in relation to the sensory trigeminal nuclei.

A trigeminal nerve is present in all vertebrates. In aquatic forms only a descending nucleus is present. Its cells are scattered and resemble those of the sub-nucleus caudalis. In amphibians a main sensory nucleus appears which is associated with the first appearance of encapsulated receptors and the descending nucleus begins to show some indication of subdivisions. This differentiation continues through birds and reptiles until the mammalian condition is reached. A mesencephalic nucleus is present in all but cyclostomes where its absence is due to the lack of jaw musculature. Early in phylogeny the sensory nuclei establish connections with the important centers for motor integration in the reticular formation, cerebellum, and tectum. Only mammals have a trigeminal lemniscus which terminates in the thalamus. This is related to the development of a neocortex, but the connections with the lower centers are maintained.

In cases of intractable lacerating pain from the face (trigeminal neuralgia, tic douloureux) the sensory root of the trigeminal nerve may be surgically sectioned or, since the pain fibers terminate in the subnucleus caudalis, the descending root may be cut low in the medulla, thus lessening the possibility of injury to other nerve roots. The spinothalamic tract is adjacent to the descending root in the medulla, and both may be involved in the same lesion. The result will be a loss of sense of pain and temperature change on the opposite side of the body since the secondary fibers of the spinothalamic tract cross in the spinal cord. There will be a loss of sense of pain and temperature change on the same side of the head due to the fact the primary fibers of the descending root are uncrossed.

7

Visceral Afferents and Referred Pain

Visceral afferents are divided into two functional components, general and special. The general conduct impulses arising from blood vessels and body cavity viscera, while the special are associated with the chemical senses of taste and smell. Olfactory pathways will be discussed in a later chapter.

The receptors in the general visceral afferent system are naked nerve endings, which respond to stretch and ischemia but not to cutting or burning. Those fibers that convey pain from the viscera are directed into the spinal cord whereas those concerned primarily with reflex control of visceral organs enter the brain stem or sacral levels of the spinal cord. The cell bodies of the pain fibers are located in the dorsal root ganglia and are unipolar. The central process enters by way of the lateral division of the dorsal root, bifurcates, and terminates in the intermediate gray. Secondary neurons may effect reflex connections with somatic neurons within the ventral horn and with preganglionic neurons associated with the autonomic nervous system. The pathway to higher centers for pain from the viscera is much more diffuse than that from the soma, and involves long and short fibers with numerous relays ascending bilaterally adjacent to the ventral horn. Upon reaching the brain stem the pathway continues via the reticular formation to the thalamus and hypothalamus.

General visceral afferents are carried by the VII, IX, and X cranial nerves (Fig. 8). The fibers of X are distributed to receptors in the larynx, esophagus, and viscera in the thorax and abdomen. The fibers of IX arise from receptors in the pharynx and posterior one-third of the tongue. The few fibers of VII supply sensory innervation to a portion of the palate. All the cell bodies are unipolar and located in the geniculate ganglion of VII, petrosal ganglion of IX, and nodose ganglion of X. The central processes of these ganglion cells enter the solitary fasciculus which extends from the lower pons to the obex, where a few cross the midline and ascend a short distance in the contralateral solitary fasciculus. Surrounding this tract throughout its course is the solitary nucleus. The primary fibers coursing in the fasciculus solitarius terminate in the

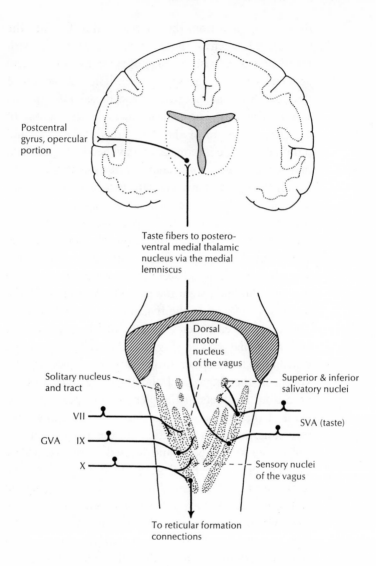

Postcentral gyrus, opercular portion

Taste fibers to postero-ventral medial thalamic nucleus via the medial lemniscus

Dorsal motor nucleus of the vagus

Solitary nucleus and tract

Superior & inferior salivatory nuclei

VII

SVA (taste)

GVA IX

X

Sensory nuclei of the vagus

To reticular formation connections

8. Visceral Afferent Pathways

solitary nucleus and dorsal sensory nucleus of X. Secondary fibers arising from these nuclei effect reflex connections with various visceral motor nuclei (autonomic); others enter the reticular formation in which are located the vital centers controlling respiration and circulation; still others ascend via reticular pathways to higher visceral centers, particularly the hypothalamus. General visceral afferents concerned with the reflex control of pelvic visceral organs have their unipolar cell bodies located in the sacral dorsal root ganglia.

Taste buds are flask-shaped and are composed of supporting and neuroepithelial (taste) cells. The apex of the taste cell reaches the surface of the tongue by way of a pore. Extending from the apex of the taste cell into the pore are hair-like processes. Taste buds are found on the tongue in relation to the papillae, the palate, and epiglottis. The terminal end of sensory nerve fibers ramify on the surface of the taste cells. The facial nerve supplies the taste buds on the anterior two-thirds of the tongue; the glossopharyngeal on the posterior one-third; and the vagus on the epiglottis. The unipolar cell bodies are located in the geniculate ganglion of VII, petrosal ganglion of IX, and nodose ganglion of X (Fig. 8). The central processes descend in the solitary fasciculus and terminate in its nucleus. In some fish, which have numerous taste buds over their bodies, this nucleus is enlarged to the point where it fuses dorsally over the fourth ventricle with its fellow of the opposite side. It is absent in many birds and greatly reduced in mammals. Secondary fibers from the solitary nucleus terminate in visceral motor nuclei, which supply salivary glands. Others cross the midline and ascend in the medial lemniscus to terminate in the posteroventral medial nucleus of the thalamus. En route some are given off to the hypothalamus. Tertiary fibers pass from the thalamus via the internal capsule and corona radiata to the primary gustatory cortex, which is located in the opercular portion of the postcentral gyrus and adjacent insular cortex.

Pain impulses arising from foci in the viscera may be interpreted as coming from a somatic area, a condition known as referred pain. Such pain is always referred from a visceral to a somatic area, both of which are supplied by the same sensory ganglion. There are several explanations why this phenomenon occurs. The viscera contain far fewer receptors per unit area than the soma, thus there is less awareness of the viscera. It has also been suggested that the incoming pain impulses from the viscera may sensitize a common neuronal pool from which both ascending visceral and somatic pathways arise. Some incoming visceral fibers may give off collaterals to the substantia gelatinosa and dorsal funicular gray, thus setting up impulses in the spinothalamic system. Another explanation is that the visceral afferent fibers effect reflex connections with the efferent fibers supplying blood vessels in the soma. This results in vasospasm, which with the accumulation of metabolic wastes stimulates the somatic sensory endings. A cordotomy to relieve visceral pain must be bilateral and extend to the ventral horn gray, since the secondary visceral tract ascends on both sides adjacent to the gray matter (fasciculus proprius).

8

Vestibular System

The receptors are neuroepithelial cells (hair cells) located in the cristae ampullaris of the semicircular canals and the maculae of the utricle and saccule of the inner ear (Fig. 9). The inner ear is in the petrous portion of the temporal bone. Although it is divided into cochlear and vestibular divisions, the structure is basically the same in that a membranous labyrinth is found within a bony enclosure, the osseous labyrinth. Otic fluid is present within the membranous labyrinth, and periotic in the osseous. The membranous portion of the vestibular division is composed of three semicircular canals which communicate with a sac-like structure, the utricle. The utricle is connected via a duct with the saccule. The point of attachment to the utricle of one arm of each of the semicircular canals is enlarged, forming the ampullae. On the wall of each ampulla is a thickening called the crista ampullaris. The cristae contain tall supporting cells and hair cells. The hairs project into a gelatinous mass, the cupula, which fills the ampulla. A portion of the wall of the utricle and saccule is thickened, forming the maculae, which are composed of supporting and hair cells and covered by a thin gelatinous mass. Embedded in the gelatinous substance are small concretions, the otoliths. Movement of the otic fluid within the semicircular canals displaces the cupula, stimulating the hair cells. In the maculae, gravity acts upon the otoliths, drawing

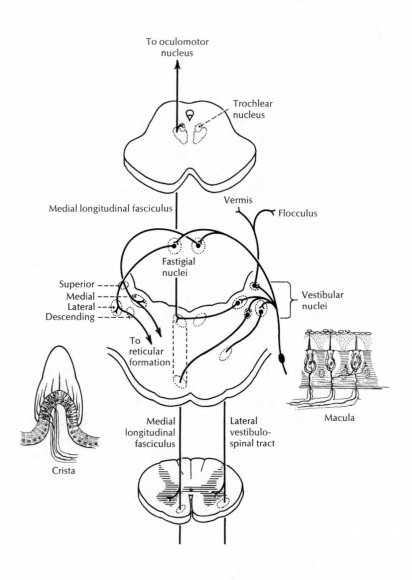

To oculomotor
nucleus

Trochlear
nucleus

Medial longitudinal fasciculus

Vermis

Flocculus

Fastigial
nuclei

Superior
Medial
Lateral
Descending

Vestibular
nuclei

To
reticular
formation

Macula

Crista

Medial
longitudinal
fasciculus

Lateral
vestibulo-
spinal tract

9. Vestibular Pathways

them against or away from the hairs of the sensory cells. Therefore, the cristae are the dynamic receptors and the maculae static receptors of the vestibular system.

The vestibular ganglion is located at the depths of the internal auditory meatus. The cells of this ganglion are bipolar. The peripheral processes terminate on the hair cells. The central processes pass in through the internal auditory meatus in company with the cochlear division of VIII and enter the brain stem at the junction of the pons and medulla. The vestibular division courses ventral and medial to the restiform body and bifurcates into ascending and descending roots. The fibers of the descending portion terminate in a synapse with the cells located in the lateral, medial, and spinal (descending) vestibular nuclei of the same side. The fibers of the ascending root terminate in the superior and medial vestibular nuclei, nucleus fastigii of the cerebellum, and the cortex of the uvula, nodulus, and flocculus of the same side. The portion of the ascending root that enters the cerebellum is a component of the juxtarestiform body.

A pathway to the cerebral cortex for the vestibular system no doubt exists, but the exact course and primary cortical area have never been conclusively demonstrated. The vestibular system is primarily concerned with the reflex maintenance of the body and its parts in relation to space. To serve this function connections are made to the extrinsic muscles of the eye, the muscles of the neck, trunk, and extremities in that order of importance. Fibers arising from the vestibular nuclei ascend and descend on both sides in the medial longitudinal fasciculus. This tract extends in a dorsomedial position from upper midbrain levels to the cervical cord, where it is found in the ventral funiculus. In the spinal cord it is frequently referred to as the medial vestibulospinal tract. Ascending fibers of the medial longitudinal fasciculus terminate in the abducens, trochlear, and oculomotor nuclei, which innervate the extraocular muscles.

Descending fibers in the medial longitudinal fasciculus enter the spinal cord and terminate on internuncial neurons in the intermediate gray. Axons from these neurons end on the ventral horn cells. By this connection the muscles of the neck and upper extremities are brought under vestibular reflex control. Another descending system of fibers arises from the lateral vestibular nucleus. It courses in the ventral and lateral funiculus and is known as the lateral vestibulospinal tract. These fibers terminate in the intermediate gray at all levels of the spinal cord. This brings the musculature of the trunk and extremities under vestibular control.

Other important projections of the vestibular nuclei are to the reticular formation and cerebellum. In addition to direct fibers from the vestibular nerve, the cerebellum receives vestibular impulses relayed by the vestibular nuclei. These fibers also enter the cerebellum by way of the juxtarestiform body and terminate in the nucleus fastigii and cortex of the flocculus, nodulus, and uvula of both sides. These areas are phylogenetically the oldest portions of the cerebellum and develop as a direct outgrowth of the vestibular nuclei. This portion of the cerebellum is vestibular in function and plays an important role in maintenance of equilibrium. The nucleus fastigii and cortical areas cited above project to the vestibular nuclei and brain-stem reticular formation of the same side by way of the juxtarestiform body. This is known as the direct fastigiobulbar tract. Some fibers from the nucleus fastigii decussate in the cerebellar commissure, loop over the brachium conjunctivum, and exit with the juxtarestiform body to end in the opposite vestibular and reticular nuclei. This bundle is known as the uncinate fasciculus. Still others cross in the cerebellum and exit with the brachium conjunctivum, ending on cells in the mid-brain tegmentum and thalamus. These fibers constitute the ascending limb of the uncinate fasciculus.

The vestibular system is one of the most stable portions of the nervous system, changing very little in phylogeny, and is present in all vertebrates. The basic pattern of connections is established in cyclostomes. In these forms the vestibular system connects with nuclei which innervate the muscles of the eye and trunk. Other projections go to the reticular formation and primordial cerebellum. The principal change in phylogeny is one of differentiation, i.e. formation of discrete tracts and nuclei.

Since the vestibular system is concerned with equilibrium, destructive lesions will result in impaired postural adjustments. If unilateral, the eyes, head, and body will turn to the affected side, and there will be vertigo and a tendency to fall to the side of the lesion. Nystagmus, a condition characterized by a slow movement of the eyes in one direction followed by a rapid return, is also present in involvement of any portion of the vestibular system. Irritative lesions result in forced movements, falling, nystagmus, vertigo (dizziness), and visceral disturbances (vomiting, sweating, etc.). The visceral disturbance is due to a discharge of the vestibular system into the reticular formation, which in turn is connected with various visceral motor nuclei. A good example of an irritative lesion is motion sickness.

9

Cochlear System

The bony cochlea consists of two and one-half turns around a central bony core, the modiolus. The osseous labyrinth is divided into two canals, the scala vestibuli and scala tympani. The membranous labyrinth, or cochlear duct, is triangular and located between the scalae, and therefore sometimes referred to as the scala media: it is separated from the scala tympani by the basilar membrane. The scala vestibuli is separated by the vestibular membrane. The scalae, which are filled with periotic fluid, communicate with each other at the apex of the cochlea through a passage called the helicotrema. The cochlear duct contains otic fluid.

The hair cells located in the organ of Corti constitute the receptors of the cochlear system (Fig. 10). The organ of Corti rests upon the basilar membrane and the hair cells are in contact with a firm fibrillar structure, the tectorial membrane. Pressure waves are set up in the periotic fluid of the scalae by movements of the foot plate of the stapes in the oval window. This results in vibration of the basilar membrane and stimulation of the hair cells via their contact with the tec-

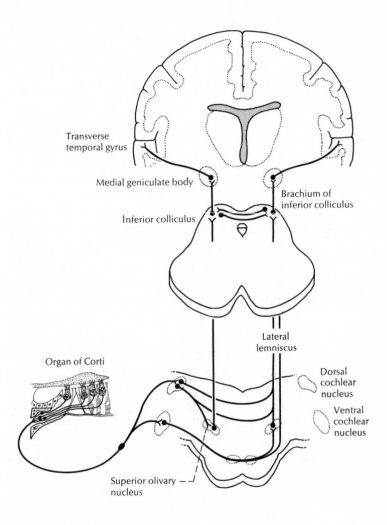

Transverse
temporal gyrus

Medial geniculate body

Brachium of
inferior colliculus

Inferior colliculus

Lateral
lemniscus

Organ of Corti

Dorsal
cochlear
nucleus

Ventral
cochlear
nucleus

Superior olivary
nucleus

10. Cochlear Pathways

torial membrane. Localization occurs in the organ of Corti in that the receptors at the apex are stimulated by low frequency sounds and at the base by high frequencies.

The cell body of the primary neuron of the auditory pathways is located in the cochlear ganglion (spiral), which is found in the modiolus. The cell bodies are bipolar, with the peripheral processes terminating in relation to the hair cells of the organ of Corti. The central process accompanies the vestibular portion of the VIIIth nerve through the internal auditory meatus to enter the brain stem at the junction of the pons and medulla. These fibers pass dorsal to the restiform body, bifurcate, and terminate in the dorsal and ventral cochlear nuclei. The dorsal nucleus forms an eminence on the dorsolateral surface of the restiform body, whereas the ventral nucleus is located lateral to the restiform body.

Secondary fibers leave the cochlear nuclei in three striae (dorsal, intermediate, ventral) which traverse the upper medulla and pons and cross the midline. The fibers of the ventral stria cross through the ascending fibers of the medial lemniscus. The point at which the ventral stria and medial lemniscus intermingle is called the trapezoid body. Many of the fibers of the three striae terminate in relation to cells in the superior olivary nucleus, accessory superior olivary nucleus, and the nucleus of the trapezoid body of both sides. Others ascend in the contralateral lateral lemniscus, which at this point includes the spinothalamic tracts. Groups of neurons are found scattered within the lateral lemniscus in the upper pons. These are the nuclei of the lateral lemniscus and constitute a nucleus of termination for some of the fibers in this lemniscus. The remaining fibers of the lateral lemniscus continue to the inferior colliculus of the midbrain, where virtually all terminate—though a few may bypass this nucleus to terminate in the medial geniculate body of the thalamus. Fibers arising from the nucleus of the inferior colliculus join those fibers of the lateral lemniscus which bypass the inferior colliculus to ascend through the brachium of the inferior colliculus (central acoustic tract) and terminate in the medial geniculate body. Fibers from the medial geniculate body course in the sublenticular portion (auditory radiations) of the internal capsule to terminate in the primary auditory cortex (superior and transverse temporal gyri).

The nuclei found throughout the course of the auditory pathway (nucleus of the trapezoid body, superior olivary nucleus, accessory superior olivary nucleus, nucleus of the lateral lemniscus, nucleus of the inferior colliculus) serve both as relay nuclei in the pathway and as reflex centers. Consequently the fibers arising from these nuclei will project forward in the auditory pathway, e.g. lateral lemniscus. Other connections of these nuclei are made with reticular nuclei, and by way of the medial longitudinal fasciculus to various motor nuclei of cranial nerves and in the intermediate gray of the spinal cord. The latter project to the ventral horn cells. These reflex connections form the basis for reflex movements of the eyes, head, and trunk in response to sound.

No secondary cochlear fibers, namely, those arising from the cochlear nuclei, can be traced into the homolateral lateral lemniscus. There is, however, bilateral representation of the acoustic system in the cerebral cortex. Tertiary fibers, such as those arising in the superior olive, therefore, may ascend uncrossed. Furthermore, there is extensive crossing between the inferior colliculi. Electrophysiological studies indicate that the nucleus of the inferior colliculus may serve as an integrative center in the acoustic pathway as well as a reflex and relay center. As already stated, other afferent tracts (spinotectal) convey impulses of pain and temperature into the inferior colliculus. Connections with the superior colliculi bring in visual impulses. This function of integration usually resides in the thalamic nuclei. Nuclei which subserve the function of integration receive many sensory modalities, which they modify and project to the cortex, thus making it possible to utilize several afferent systems to appreciate form, texture, etc. Therefore, in the acoustic pathway the medial geniculate body apparently acts only as a cortical relay nucleus.

Efferent fibers to the organ of Corti have been described. They arise from the reticular formation in the vicinity of the superior olivary nucleus, course as the olivary peduncle to the region of the abducens nucleus, where they are both crossed and uncrossed and exit with the VIIIth nerve. These terminate in relation to the hair cells of the organ of Corti. By this means the central nervous system can regulate the input from the organ of Corti by altering the threshold of the receptors.

All vertebrates respond to pressure waves in the atmosphere or water, but only in mammals is a true cochlea present. The lateral line system, which consists of hair cells located in pits, grooves, or canals on the surface of the body, serves as the receptor for low frequencies in submammalian aquatic forms. In some fish the incipient beginnings of a receptor area in the inner ear may be present. Fibers of the lateral line nerves terminate in a nuclear group dorsal to the vestibular nuclei. These project to the reticular formation and the roof of the midbrain, although no inferior colliculus is present. In reptiles and birds a definite receptor area, the lagena papilla (forerunner of the cochlea), is present in the inner ear. Central connections and pathways are the same as aquatic forms, although there is more differentiation. Only in mammals are a cochlea, dorsal and ventral cochlear nuclei, inferior colliculus, medial geniculate body, and auditory cortex present.

Unilateral lesions that completely destroy the receptors, cochlear nerve, or cochlear nuclei will cause total deafness in that ear. Central unilateral lesions (cortex, medial geniculate body, lateral lemniscus) result in impaired hearing in both ears, but more marked on the opposite side. Isolated lesions of specific parts of the organ of Corti may result in deafness to a specific pitch or tone. Conduction deafness results from involvement of those organs conducting sound waves to the receptor, e.g. ear ossicles, but bone conduction is not impaired in those cases, i.e. a tuning fork placed on the skull can be heard. Irritative lesions result in hissing and roaring sounds. These usually precede a destructive lesion.

10

Visual System

The retina, which contains the light receptors, is the innermost layer of the eye. Embryologically, it is formed from an evagination of the diencephalon. Three basic types of nerve cells are present in the retina: rod and cone cells, bipolar cells, and ganglion cells (Fig. 11). The outermost are the rod and cone cells, whose dendrites are modified to form rods and cones. The rods, numbering over 100 million, are slender elongated modifications of the dendritic end. The cones, of which there are about 7 million, are shorter and thicker. In the center of the retina is a circular yellowish spot, the macula lutea, which is depressed in the middle, forming the fovea centralis. The fovea contains only cones and is devoid of any other retinal layer. The cones decrease in number toward the periphery, whereas the rods increase. The cones are for brightness discrimination and color vision. The rods are concerned with dimness and peripheral vision.

Outside the rods and cones is a layer of pigmented cells. Light striking the retina causes these cells to stimulate the rods and cones chemically. The pigment migrates with varying degrees of illumination, increasing in amount between the receptors in bright light.

Central to the rod and cone cells is a layer of bipolar neurons. Their dendrites synapse with the axons of the receptor cells. Inside the layer of bipolar neurons are

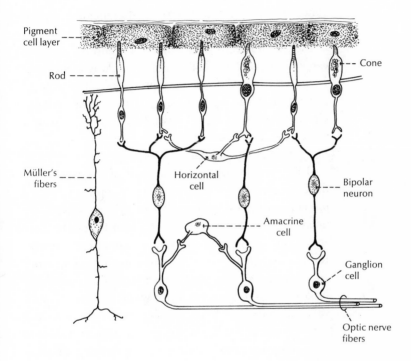

Pigment cell layer

Rod

Cone

Müller's fibers

Horizontal cell

Bipolar neuron

Amacrine cell

Ganglion cell

Optic nerve fibers

Based on an original drawing by Biagio Melloni

11. Histology of the Retina

located the ganglion cells, which are multipolar neurons in synaptic relation with the bipolar cells. There is a one-to-one relationship between the cones in the fovea, bipolar neurons, and ganglion cells, whereas in the periphery there is a progressive convergence of rods and cones on one bipolar neuron and numerous bipolar neurons synapsing with one ganglion cell. The axons of the ganglion cells gather in a layer centrally and converge on a point medial to the fovea, where they exit from the eye and form the optic nerve. The area of convergence, the optic papilla, is devoid of receptor elements, so that light waves falling on the papilla cannot be perceived. This area is designated as the blind spot of the retina.

Other neurons which are not part of the direct conduction path from the receptors to optic nerve are present within the retina (horizontal, centrifugal, bipolar, and amacrine cells). The dendrites of the horizontal cells are in relation to the synaptic zone between the rod and cone cells and bipolar neurons. The axons are in contact with rods and cones. The centrifugal bipolar neuron synapses by way of a dendrite with ganglion cells. The axon ramifies among the rods and cones. Amacrine cells do not have a distinct axon and their processes ramify among the bipolar and ganglion cells. The amacrine cells may be concerned with reverberating circuits within the retina.

Efferent fibers to the retina have been described. These terminate in relation to rods and cones, bipolar, ganglion, and amacrine cells. They may alter the threshold of the receptor and have an influence on synaptic transmission within the retina.

Since the retina is an extension of the central nervous system, it also contains neuroglia. Processes of these cells ramify throughout the retina. They also form two membranes: the outer limiting membrane, which is between the rods and cones and their cell bodies; the inner limiting membrane, which separates the layer of optic nerve fibers from the vitreous body.

Due to the arrangement of cells, fibers, and synaptic areas, ten retinal layers can be recognized. The outermost is the layer of pigment cells (1). Adjacent to this are the rods and cones (2), followed by the outer limiting membrane (3). The outer nuclear layer (4) consists of the cell bodies of the rod and cone cells. The synaptic zone between the rod and cone cells and bipolar neurons is the outer plexiform layer (5). Adjacent to this is the inner nuclear layer (6), which consists largely of bipolar cells. The inner plexiform layer (7) is the synaptic zone between bipolar and ganglion cells. The multipolar neurons form the ganglionic cell layer (8), and their axons form the layer of optic nerve fibers (9). Finally, the inner limiting membrane (10) separates the retina from the vitreous body. Therefore, to reach the rods and cones, light must penetrate the ten retinal layers except at the fovea centralis.

The optic nerve, like the retina, is an extension of the central nervous system and is, therefore, not a true nerve. It courses through the optic foramen to the optic chiasma, where half the fibers decussate (Fig. 12). From the optic chiasma the fibers are known as the optic tract, which passes back to enter the diencephalon, where most of the fibers terminate in the lateral geniculate body. The axons of the cells in the lateral geniculate body give rise to the optic radiations. These course in the retrolenticular portion of the internal

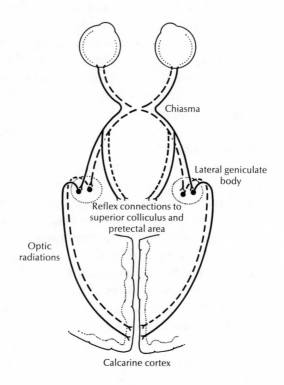

Chiasma

Lateral geniculate body

Reflex connections to superior colliculus and pretectal area

Optic radiations

Calcarine cortex

12. Visual Pathways

capsule in the lateral wall of the inferior horn of the lateral ventricle to the calcarine cortex (cuneus and lingual gyri).

There is a point-to-point relationship between specific quadrants of the retina and specific parts along the optic pathway. Fibers from the medial half of the retina and medial half of the macula course in the medial half of the optic nerve and cross in the optic chiasma to the medial half of the opposite optic tract. Fibers from the macula occupy the center of the optic nerve and tract. Fibers from the lateral half of the retina and lateral half of the macula course in the lateral half of the optic nerve and optic tract of the same side. They do not cross in the optic chiasma. Fibers from the macula terminate in the posterior superior portion of the lateral geniculate body. Fibers from the lower quadrants of the retina end in the lateral portion of the lateral geniculate body. Fibers of the optic radiations conveying impuses from the upper quadrants of the retina course in the superior part of the radiations and terminate in the cuneus, the superior part of the calcarine cortex. The inferior fibers of the radiations convey impulses from the lower quadrants of the retina to the lingual gyrus, the inferior part of the calcarine cortex. Fibers of the radiations conveying impulses from the macula occupy an intermediate position, and terminate in the posterior portion of the calcarine cortex.

It must be remembered that the visual and retinal fields are reversed. Light from below a horizontal plane, passing through the center of the pupil, falls on the upper retinal quadrants. Light from above this plane falls on the lower retinal quadrants. Light from the right falls on the nasal retina of the right eye and temporal retina of the left eye. Light from the left falls on the nasal retina of the left eye and temporal retina of the right eye. Therefore, since the fibers from the nasal retina cross in the optic chiasma, the left visual field is represented in the right optic tract, lateral geniculate body, optic radiations, and calcarine cortex. The right visual field is represented in the left optic tract, etc.

A few fibers of the optic tract bypass the lateral geniculate body to enter the brachium of the superior colliculus and terminate in the superior colliculus and pretectal region. These fibers are joined by a few arising from the lateral geniculate body. Fibers from the superior colliculus and pretectal region terminate in the parasympathetic portion of the IIIrd nerve nucleus (Edinger-Westphal). This is the anatomical basis for the pupillary constriction reflex to light. From the pretectal region and superior colliculus, fibers descend via the medial longitudinal fasciculus, tectospinal tract, and by short relays through the reticular formation, to the intermediolateral cell column of the upper thoracic segments. This is the basis for the dilator reflex to light. The accommodation reflex, which includes pupillary constriction, thickening of the lens, and convergence of the eyes, involves a pathway through the cerebral cortex. There are other reflexes to light, involving reflex movement of the eyes, head, etc., which have diffuse pathways but which apparently arise from the pretectal region and superior colliculus. Some fibers cross in the posterior commissure, resulting in crossed reflexes.

The structure of the retina is basically the same in all vertebrates. The optic nerve, chiasma, and tract are likewise constant. However, only in those mammals with binocular vision is there partial crossing in the chiasma. In all other vertebrates the decussation is complete. An optic tectum is present in all forms but is known as the superior colliculus only in mammals. The basic reflex pathways are established early but projections to the cortex occur only in birds and mammals. Since cortical representation of sensory systems is a mammalian feature only, the presence in birds is unusual.

A complete lesion of the optic nerve will result in total blindness in that eye. If the optic tract is severed, however, the defect will be in the opposite visual field since fibers from the nasal retina cross. This is known as homonymous hemianopsia. The same condition results from the total destruction of the lateral geniculate body, optic radiations, or visual cortex. A lesion of the optic chiasma interrupting only the decussating fibers results in bitemporal hemianopsia, i.e. the temporal portion of the visual field of each eye is affected. Destruction of the superior portion of the optic radiations or cuneus results in opposite lower quadrantic defects, whereas involvement of the lower radiations or lingual gyrus gives rise to opposite upper quadrantic defects. Lesions of the pretectal region and/or superior colliculus abolish reflexes to light but do not impair visual acuity. If the posterior commissure is involved, crossed reflexes are absent.

11

Dorsal Thalamus

The diencephalon is divided into four divisions: epithalamus, hypothalamus, subthalamus, and dorsal thalamus. The epithalamus has strong connections with the olfactory system and will be discussed in Chapter 18. The hypothalamus is associated with basic vegetative functions and will be covered under the autonomic nervous system. The subthalamus is related to the extrapyramidal system. The dorsal thalamus is composed of a number of nuclei, most of which have numerous subdivisions. It is not within the scope of this work to discuss exhaustively all the nuclei—only the major nuclear groups will be covered.

The internal medullary lamina of the dorsal thalamus separates the nuclei into two major groups: the medial-anterior group and lateral-ventral group (Fig. 13). The lamina is composed of myelinated fibers entering or leaving the adjacent thalamic nuclei. The external medullary lamina is medial to the internal capsule. Its fibers interconnect the thalamic nuclei with the cerebral cortex.

The anterior nucleus has extensive reciprocal connections with the gyrus cinguli, but its principal afferent tract is the mammillothalamic fasciculus. Some fibers of the fornix also end in this nucleus. Since the gyrus cinguli is a portion of the limbic lobe, which is concerned with autonomic functions and emotional

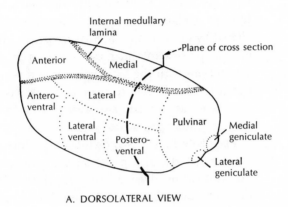

A. DORSOLATERAL VIEW

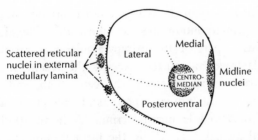

B. CROSS SECTION TO SHOW RETICULAR NUCLEI

13. Dorsal Thalamus

tone, the anterior nucleus plays an important role in these activities.

The medial (dorsomedial) nucleus has extensive reciprocal connections with the prefrontal lobes, and also receives numerous fibers from hypothalamus and posteroventral nucleus of the thalamus. The prefrontal lobes are related to personality, ideation, and affective tone, i.e. feeling of well being. These states are readily altered by external and internal sensations. The medial nucleus plays a role in these functions by way of its connections with the hypothalamus and posteroventral nucleus. The former receives extensive visceral afferents, whereas the latter is associated with the main somatic sensory pathways.

The ventral nucleus is divisible into three segments: anterior, lateral, and posterior; the posterior segment can further be divided into medial and lateral. All three portions are important cortical relay nuclei which receive ascending fibers and project to the cortex. The anteroventral receives a strong input from the globus pallidus by way of the thalamic fasciculus and projects to the primary motor and premotor cortex. The globus pallidus is part of the extrapyramidal motor system. The lateroventral nucleus receives the brachium conjunctivum which arises in the cerebellum, and also projects to the primary motor and premotor cortex. The trigeminal lemniscus terminates in the posteroventral medial nucleus and the medial lemniscus and spinothalamic tracts end in the posteroventral lateral. Both these nuclei send fibers to the postcentral gyrus.

The strongest connections of the lateral nucleus are with the posterior portion of the parietal lobe and pass in both directions. The lateral nucleus also is related to adjacent thalamic nuclei. Since the posterior parietal lobe is an important association area concerned with interpreting and integrating various sensory modalities, the lateral nucleus plays a role in reinforcing these functions.

The pulvinar and medial and lateral geniculate bodies may also be included in the lateral and ventral group of thalamic nuclei. The two geniculate bodies are primarily cortical relay nuclei. The medial geniculate body receives the brachium of the inferior colliculus and projects as auditory radiations to the primary auditory cortex. The optic tract terminates in the lateral geniculate body, which gives rise to the optic radiations terminating in the primary visual cortex.

The pulvinar is associated with the posterior parietal, lateral occipital, and posterior temporal cortices. The connections are two-way. These cortical areas are association centers, and thus the pulvinar is related to these functions. The pulvinar has very few connections with other thalamic nuclei.

The dorsal thalamus contains, in addition, three poorly defined nuclear groups: reticular, intralaminar, and midline. The reticular nuclei, which are scattered patches of cells in the external medullary lamina, have strong connections with the brain-stem reticular formation. They are considered to be part of the ascending reticular activating system. The intralaminar nuclei are located within the internal medullary lamina. One portion is well developed, forming the discrete centromedian nucleus. These nuclei, which have extensive connections with other thalamic nuclei and basal ganglia, function as coordinators of the thalamic nuclei. The midline nuclei are gray masses in the wall of the third ventricle and include the massa intermedia, which bridges the ventricle. They are associated with the hypothalamus and basal ganglia and are related to basic vegetative functions.

The nuclei associated primarily with subcortical areas (midline and intralaminar) are phylogenetically the oldest. Homologues of these nuclei exist in all vertebrates. The same is true of the reticular nuclei, since the ascending reticular activating system is phylogenetically old. The anterior nucleus projects to the limbic lobe, which is paleocortex. It is present in reptiles and birds. Those nuclei which relay to neocortical areas (ventral nucleus and geniculate bodies) make their appearance in mammals. The nuclei that are reciprocally related with highly developed association cortex (pulvinar, lateral, and medial) are phylogenetically the newest. They may be present in most mammals but are prominent only in the higher primates.

Due to the multiplicity of functions of the dorsal thalamus a wide variety of signs and symptoms may result from destructive lesions. Intellectual deterioration may occur. Personality changes occur with the destruction of the medial nucleus. If the lesion encroaches on the posteroventral nucleus there is contralateral loss of position sense and touch discrimination. Ataxia, an awkward gait, is present due to loss of knowledge of the position of the limbs. Awareness of pain and of temperature persist but are poorly localized; the feeling of pain may be greatly exaggerated. Involvement of the lateral geniculate body gives rise to homonymous hemianopsia.

12

Lower Motor Neurons and General Aspects of Motor Systems

Nuclei giving rise to fibers innervating skeletal muscle derived from myotomes are referred to as general somatic efferent. Special visceral efferent fibers supply skeletal muscles of branchial arch origin. General visceral efferents innervate the viscera and will be discussed in the chapter on the autonomic nervous system. The general somatic efferent column of cells is adjacent to the midline directly under the cerebral aqueduct, fourth ventricle, and ventrolateral to the central canal. It is represented in the midbrain by the oculomotor nucleus, which innervates the superior palpebral, inferior oblique, and superior, medial, and inferior rectus muscles of the eye (Fig. 14). The trochlear nucleus is in the lower midbrain. It supplies the superior oblique muscle of the eye. The abducens nucleus, which innervates the lateral rectus, is located in the lower pons. The hypoglossal nucleus, whose fibers supply the intrinsic muscles of the tongue, is found throughout a considerable extent of the medulla. The general somatic efferent column in the spinal cord is represented by the ventral horn. It innervates the muscles of the trunk and extremities. The fibers of all these nuclei exit ventrally except those of the trochlear, which, after decussating, emerge caudal to the inferior colliculus on the dorsal aspect of the brain stem.

The special visceral efferent column of cells is ventral and lateral to the general somatic efferent group. Fibers

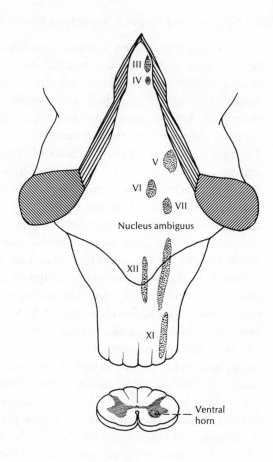

III
IV
V
VI
VII
Nucleus ambiguus
XII
XI
Ventral
horn

14. Lower Motor Nuclei

arising from these nuclei course for a variable distance dorsally and medially, turn sharply back, forming a loop, and exit laterally. The motor nucleus of the trigeminal nerve is located in the upper pons and supplies the muscles of mastication, which come from the first branchial arch. The facial nucleus, whose fibers innervate the facial muscles, is in the lower pons. These muscles are derived from the second branchial arch. The nucleus ambiguus consists of a thin column of cells extending throughout most of the medulla. Fibers from the cephalic portion supply the stylopharyngeus muscle by way of the glossopharyngeal nerve. This muscle arises embryologically from the third branchial arch. Fibers from the caudal portion of the nucleus ambiguus join the vagus nerve to innervate the muscles of the larynx, pharynx, and upper esophagus. These muscles develop from the fourth and fifth arches. The accessory nucleus is located in the lower medulla and upper cervical segments of the spinal cord and supplies portions of the sternocleidomastoid and trapezius muscles, which are derived in part from the caudal portion of the branchial arch system.

Each motor fiber terminates in relation to a motor end plate found on the muscle fiber. The surface of the muscle fiber covered with sarcolemma is thrown into folds, forming clefts in between the elevations. The nerve fiber as it approaches the muscle divides into a variable number of branches and loses its myelin sheath. The terminal end of the nerve fiber retains its neurilemma and sends branches into the clefts on the muscle fiber. Surrounding the motor end plate in the adjacent sarcoplasm is a concentration of nuclei. The nerve fiber terminals contain mitochondria and synaptic vesicles which in turn contain the transmitter substance. A single efferent neuron plus the muscle fibers it innervates constitute a motor unit. The ratio of muscle fibers to the motor neuron becomes progressively smaller with the degree to which the muscles are capable of carrying out fine discrete movements.

Cells within the motor nuclei are frequently referred to as lower motor neurons or the final common path. All motor systems, from reflex mechanisms to voluntary motor activity, must converge on these neurons for their influences to reach the effectors. Descending tracts from higher centers (supranuclear or upper motor neurons) or afferent fibers of peripheral nerves do not terminate, with few exceptions, directly upon the lower motor neuron. Instead they end in relation to the intermediate gray and the base of the dorsal horn in the spinal cord, and in the reticular formation surrounding the motor nuclei in the brain stem. Cells in these areas synapse with the motor neurons. The exceptions to the general rule include some of the fibers of the pyramidal tract (the voluntary motor system) and a few sensory fibers of peripheral nerves mediating the myotatic reflex.

Since all motor systems and afferents from peripheral receptors converge on the intermediate gray and reticular formation, these areas become important correlation and integration centers. All the systems above play an important role in motor activity and are in delicate balance with each other since there are numerous feedback circuits between the higher centers. In any motor act they all send information to the reticular formation and intermediate gray, which correlates this information and projects the final pattern on the lower motor neurons. These in turn conduct the impulses to the appropriate receptors.

If the lower motor neurons are destroyed, such as in lesions of the peripheral nerves or motor nuclei, total paralysis of the muscles supplied by these cells results. No impulses can reach the muscles, which are thus completely flaccid. Reflexes are absent. If the lesion involves upper motor neurons, the muscles are not completely paralyzed since the lower motor neurons are intact and some impulses still reach the muscles. However, since all motor centers play a role in motor activity, destruction of one destroys the delicate balance between them, and the normal pattern of motor activity is altered. The affected muscles still exhibit some tone, but they may be hypertonic (spasticity or rigidity) or hypotonic depending on the location of the lesion; and there may be hyper- or hyporeflexia. Other symptoms present may be the paralysis of some movements and presence of abnormal movements.

13

Cerebellum

The cerebellum overrides the medulla and pons and is overlapped by the occipital lobes of the cerebral hemispheres. Two cerebellar hemispheres can be recognized, separated by a midline vermis. The cerebellum can be divided into numerous lobules but for the purpose of this work only three major lobes will be recognized. The first fissure to appear is the uvulonodular and its hemispheric extension, the posterolateral fissure. Posterior to these fissures is the flocculonodular lobe. The nodulus is vermis, and the flocculi hemispheric. On the superior surface of the cerebellum is found the primary fissure. The anterior lobe is forward to this. The posterior lobe, composing the largest portion of the cerebellum, is located between the primary and uvulonodular fissures. The flocculonodular lobe is phylogenetically the oldest portion of the cerebellum and is associated with the vestibular system. It is referred to as archicerebellum. The anterior lobe along with the uvula and pyramis in the posterior vermal portion of the posterior lobe constitute the paleocerebellum. It is related principally to gross movements of the head and body. The remainder of the posterior lobe makes up the neocerebellum, which develops in relation to the neocortex. It is thus associated with finer voluntary movements.

The surface of the cerebellum is thrown into numerous transverse folds known as folia. The cortex is located superficially (Fig. 15A). The central core of the cerebellum contains white matter, at the base of which are the deep cerebellar nuclei (Fig. 15B). The structure of the cortex is uniform. It consists of three layers which, from superficial to deep, are: molecular layer, Purkinje (ganglionic) cell layer, and granule cell layer. The molecular layer contains principally dendrites and axons of cells in the deeper layers. It is thus an important synaptic zone. Present within this zone are a few neurons known as basket cells. The axons course at right angles to the long axes of the folia. Collaterals and terminals form basket-like synaptic endings around the Purkinje cells. The Purkinje cells

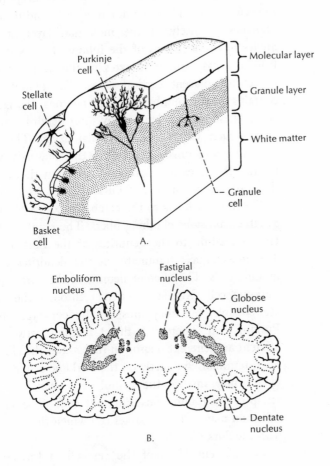

A.

B.

15. Cerebellar Cortex and Cerebellar Nuclei

are large neurons forming a single layer deep to the molecular layer. They contain an apical dendrite which branches profusely in the molecular layer at right angles to the long axis of the folium. The axon arises from the base and terminates in the deep cerebellar nuclei or adjacent cortical areas. The granule layer contains a large number of small neurons, the granule cells. These neurons have many short dendrites and an axon which enters the molecular layer. The axon bifurcates and runs parallel with the long axis of the folium. It comes into synaptic contact with the dendrites of a large number of Purkinje cells.

The afferent fibers to the cerebellar cortex terminate as either mossy or climbing fibers. The climbing fibers end in relation to the dendrites of the Purkinje cell. The mossy fibers terminate on the dendrites of the granule cells. The efferent neuron of the cortex is the Purkinje cell. Numerous circuits through the cortex are possible, but they must finally converge on the Purkinje cell. There is a direct relation between the afferent and efferent neuron in the case of the climbing fiber, terminating directly on the Purkinje cell. Another circuit may involve the granule cell, which in turn synapses with numerous Purkinje cells. The granule cell axon may end on a basket cell which then synapses with the Purkinje cell.

The afferent fibers of the cerebellum traverse the three cerebellar peduncles (Fig. 16). The inferior cerebellar peduncle is entirely afferent with the exception of its medial portion, which is designated the juxtarestiform body. This was discussed in the chapter on the vestibular system. Other components of the inferior

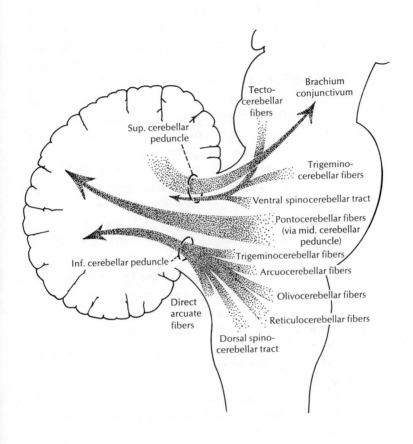

Tecto-cerebellar fibers

Brachium conjunctivum

Sup. cerebellar peduncle

Trigemino-cerebellar fibers

Ventral spinocerebellar tract

Pontocerebellar fibers (via mid. cerebellar peduncle)

Trigeminocerebellar fibers

Arcuocerebellar fibers

Olivocerebellar fibers

Reticulocerebellar fibers

Inf. cerebellar peduncle

Direct arcuate fibers

Dorsal spino-cerebellar tract

16. Cerebellar Connections

peduncle are: dorsal spinocerebellar tract, olivocerebellar fibers, trigeminocerebellar fibers, direct arcuate fibers, arcuocerebellar fibers, and a reticulocerebellar component. The dorsal spinocerebellar tract arises from the homolateral nucleus dorsalis in the thoracic cord. This nucleus receives terminals from the dorsal funiculus and constitutes a pathway to the cerebellum for exteroceptive and proprioceptive impulses. The dorsal spinocerebellar tract terminates in the vermis. The olivocerebellar fibers originate in the inferior olivary nucleus in the medulla, are entirely crossed, and terminate in most areas of the cerebellar cortex. The inferior olivary nucleus receives fibers from two sources: spino-olivary tract and central tegmental fasciculus. The spino-olivary tract arises from the contralateral dorsal horn. The spino-olivocerebellar pathway may constitute another pathway to the cerebellum for touch and proprioception. The central tegmental fasciculus has a diffuse origin from midbrain and diencephalic nuclei. These nuclei probably belong to the extrapyramidal system. The central tegmental tract descends through the center of the brain stem to terminate in the inferior olivary nucleus.

The trigeminocerebellar fibers arise from the subnuclei interpolaris and rostralis of the descending nucleus of V. They are both crossed and uncrossed and terminate in the vermis. This is the pathway for tactile impulse from the head to the cerebellum. Direct arcuate fibers arise from the homolateral external cuneate nucleus. They also terminate in the vermis. Since this nucleus receives terminals from the fasciculus cuneatus, the direct arcuate fibers are in the pathway from the proprioceptors and tactile receptors in the neck and upper extremities to the cerebellum. The arcuate nuclei are found in the medullary pyramid and are probably displaced pontine nuclei. They receive fibers from the homolateral motor cortex and are concerned with relating that area to the cerebellum. Arcuocerebellar fibers cross the midline and circle the periphery of the medulla as ventral external arcuate fibers. They end in the cerebellar hemispheres. The reticular nuclei project into the cerebellum from both sides, either directly or by way of the ventral external arcuate fibers. They have diffuse terminations in the cortex. The reticular formation has spinoreticular connections as well as connections from a number of other sensory systems. It serves as a relay station for a variety of sensory modalities to the cerebellum.

The middle cerebellar peduncle is likewise entirely afferent and contains one component, the pontocerebellar fibers. These are entirely crossed and arise from the pontine nuclei. They terminate in the neocerebellar cortex of the hemispheres. A large bundle of fibers, the corticopontine tract, arises from the motor cortex and descends uncrossed to terminate in the pontine nuclei. The corticopontocerebellar pathway is an important link between the motor areas of the neocortex and the neocerebellum.

The superior cerebellar peduncle is mixed, the efferent component being the largest. It will be discussed below. The ventral spinocerebellar tract arises from scattered cells of the dorsal and intermediate gray of the spinal cord of both sides. It ascends ventral to the dorsal tract, but in the medulla when the dorsal tract enters the inferior peduncle it continues to the upper pons, loops back, and enters the cerebellum with the superior peduncle to terminate in the vermis. It forms another pathway for exteroceptive and proprioceptive impulses from the body to the cerebellum. The main sensory nucleus of the trigeminal nerve sends some fibers to the cerebellar vermis by way of the superior peduncle. This is another link between somatic receptors in the head and the cerebellum. The tectocerebellar tract arising from the superior and inferior colliculi convey visual and auditory impressions into the cerebellum by way of the superior peduncle.

Four pairs of nuclei can be recognized in the medullary core at the base of the cerebellum. They are, from medial to lateral: fastigial, globosus, emboliformis, and dentate. The connections of the nucleus fastigii with the flocculonodular lobe, vestibular nuclei, and reticular formation have been discussed in the chapter on the vestibular system. The globosus and emboliformis nuclei are small. A portion of the globosus is related to the vestibular system while the remainder, and the emboliformis nuclei, have the same connections as the dentate. The dentate is a large convoluted nucleus which receives fibers from the Purkinje cells of the cerebellar cortex. The dentate nucleus gives rise to a compact bundle of fibers, the superior cerebellar peduncle, which courses cephalically in the superior medullary velum. In the upper pons and lower midbrain the superior cerebellar peduncle turns ventral and medial to decussate with its fellow of the opposite side.

After crossing, a small bundle of fibers is given off which descends through the tegmentum of the midbrain and pons and reticular formation of the medulla. This is the crossed descending limb of the brachium conjunctivum. It terminates in relation to nuclear groups in the tegmentum and reticular formation.

The remaining fibers, constituting the crossed ascending limb of the brachium conjunctivum, course through and around the red nucleus. A number of the fibers terminate here and the remainder continue into the thalamus to end in the lateroventral nucleus. This nucleus projects through the internal capsule to the motor areas of the cortex. It also sends fibers into the basal ganglia, thereby completing feedback circuits between the cerebellum and the motor cortex and basal ganglia.

The red nucleus projects both cephalically and caudally. Ascending fibers intermingle with those of the brachium conjunctivum to terminate in the lateroventral nucleus of the thalamus. Descending fibers cross ventral to the red nucleus and descend as the rubrospinal tract in the lateral portion of the brain stem and lateral funiculus of the spinal cord, terminating in the intermediate gray. Other descending fibers contribute to the central tegmental fasciculus to end in the inferior olivary nucleus.

The cerebellum is present in cyclostomes where it forms a plate of cells bridging the fourth ventricle between the acousticolateral areas. Its afferent connections are with the vestibular and lateral line systems and the trigeminal and tectal nuclei. Although there are no basal nuclei present, diffuse cells in the cerebellar plate project to the reticular formation. An auricular lobe, the homologue of the flocculus, and a vermis are present in cartilaginous fish. The auricular lobe is the only portion of the hemispheres present in submammals. There is a well-developed spinocerebellar system which is associated with the development of the vermis and coordination of the trunk muscles. Only one pair of basal nuclei is present in cartilaginous fish. The corticopontocerebellar system, cerebellar hemispheres, dentate nucleus, dentatorubrothalamic system, and projections to motor cortex are present only in mammals. These structures are related to the development of the neocortex and coordination of fine movements.

The function of the cerebellum can best be summarized by the word "synergy," thus the deficits resulting from cerebellar disease are related to asynergy. Asynergy is expressed in such conditions as an awkward gait (ataxia), hypotonia, hyporeflexia, dysmetria (missing the mark), jerky and explosive speech, and asthenia. An intention tremor is present when the dentate nucleus or brachium conjunctivum is involved. All signs and symptoms are on the same side as the lesion.

14

Pyramidal System

Classically, the pyramidal system is considered to be the voluntary motor system controlling fine digital movements. The axons of this system arise from pyramidal cells in the fifth layer of the cortex in the precentral gyrus and premotor area (Fig. 17). The fibers descend through the corona radiata, posterior limb of the internal capsule, and occupy the middle three-fifths of the basis pedunculi of the midbrain. From midbrain levels on down through the pons and medulla, fibers leave

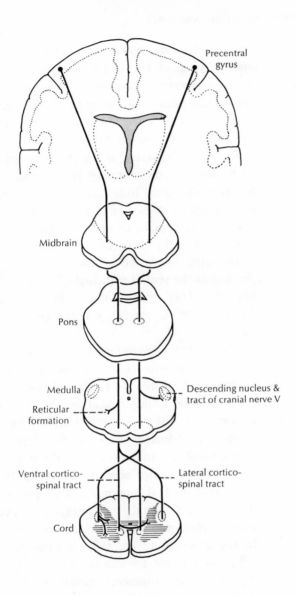

17. Pyramidal System

the main tract and some terminate in motor nuclei of cranial nerves of both sides, constituting the cortico-bulbar component. Those remaining continue through the basilar portion of the pons. In the medulla the fibers form a compact bundle adjacent to the ventral midline forming the medullary pyramid. In the lower medulla the fibers cross, as fascicles interdigitating with each other. Upon attaining the opposite side they gather in the lateral funiculus of the spinal cord, form-ing the lateral corticospinal tract, which extends the length of the spinal cord and terminates in the ventral horn. Most of the fibers end in the cervical and lumbo-sacral enlargements, but a few remain uncrossed and descend as the ventral corticospinal tract in the ventral funiculus. They descend only to lower cervical levels. Most cross to the opposite side and end in the ventral horn.

There is topographical representation of the body on the precentral gyrus. The head area is located latero-ventrally and adjacent to the lateral fissure. The lower extremity is dorsal and medial and the upper extremity intermediate. The area of representation for any group of muscles is directly related to the degree to which they control fine movements, i.e. the finer the move-ment the greater area of cortex devoted to the muscles responsible for that movement. Most muscles are rep-resented in the contralateral cortex. Some have bilateral representation and others virtually no representation. In the latter group are those muscles largely under reflex control (extra-ocular muscles) or those respon-sible for gross movements (proximal muscles of the trunk and extremities). The muscles with contralateral representation are those of the extremities and lower half of the face. The muscles of mastication, muscles of the tongue, and sternocleidomastoid and trapezius have varying degrees of bilateral representation. The laryngeal and pharyngeal muscles, the muscles in the upper half of the face, and those in the diaphragm are bilaterally represented.

Although some of the fibers of the pyramidal system in higher primates follow the origin, course, and termination outlined above, many others present a different pattern. Fibers descending in the traditional pyramidal pathway arise from a number of areas of the cortex outside the precentral gyrus. The premotor cortex, which is forward to the precentral gyrus, contributes a large number, the primary somesthetic cortex makes a substantial contribution, and other cortical areas have also been implicated.

Most of the fibers of the pyramidal system terminate in areas outside the lower motor neurons. In the spinal cord many fibers end in the intermediate gray and base of the dorsal horn. As stated in Chapter 12, this neuronal pool is an important integrating center, receiving an input from all motor areas. It in turn projects to the ventral horn. In the brain stem, numerous fibers can be traced into the reticular formation, particularly in areas adjacent to the motor nuclei of cranial nerves. The reticular formation is the integrator at this level. A substantial number of fibers from the pyramidal tract terminate in, or adjacent to, sensory relay nuclei such as the nucleus cuneatus, nucleus gracilis, and descending nucleus of the trigeminal nerve. This provides a feedback to these nuclei from the sensorimotor cortex. Thus the cortex may in some way regulate sensory input.

The pyramidal system is present only in mammals. In the lowest forms the excitable motor cortex is poorly organized as regards topographical localization and overlaps extensively with the sensory cortex. Due to the absence of prefrontal lobes in lower mammals the sensorimotor cortex is located near the frontal pole. This area becomes progressively more organized and is pushed back by the developing prefrontal lobes. The course of the tract through the brain stem is uniform but in the spinal cord most of the fibers are found in the contralateral dorsal funiculus in lower mammals. It switches progressively to the lateral funiculus. The tract descends to lumbar and sacral levels except in marsupials, in which it reaches only the lower cervical cord. Termination is in the reticular formation, intermediate gray, and sensory relay nuclei in all but higher primates. In the higher primates some fibers can be traced directly to the lower motor neuron. This connection is associated with the acquisition of finer movements.

Lesions of the pyramidal tract cause spastic paralysis and the loss of finer movements. The deep reflexes are exaggerated. Interruption of the pathway above the decussation results in contralateral deficits. If the lesion is in the spinal cord the homolateral musculature is affected; but not all muscles are affected equally, due either to poor or bilateral representation in the cortex. In the trunk and extremities following a unilateral lesion the more distal muscles exhibit the greatest degree of paralysis. The muscles of the diaphragm, larynx, pharynx, esophagus, upper half of the face, and the extraocular muscles are not affected because of bilateral cortical representation. The contralateral lower half of the face is paralyzed. The opposite muscles of mastication, and of the tongue may show various degrees of involvement.

15

Extrapyramidal System

In a broad definition, the extrapyramidal system includes all somatic motor pathways outside the pyramidal system, but only certain nuclei and tracts found at all levels of the neuraxis are usually included. The basal ganglia constitute the largest nuclear masses belonging to this system (Fig. 18). They are found at the base of the telencephalon medial to the insula and lateral to the diencephalon, and include the caudate nucleus, putamen, and globus pallidus. The putamen and globus pallidus are frequently referred to as the lenticular nucleus and all three as the corpus striatum, although the corpus striatum may be restricted to the caudate and putamen. Some investigators include the claustrum and amygdala in the basal ganglia. The claustrum is a thin lamina of gray matter situated between the extreme and external capsules. The functional relationship to the basal ganglia is not known. It may also be a portion of the insular cortex. The amygdaloid nucleus, which belongs to the olfactory and limbic systems, will be discussed in Chapter 18.

The basal ganglia are a part of ascending and descending multisynaptic pathways between cortex and lower centers, thus their afferent and efferent connec-

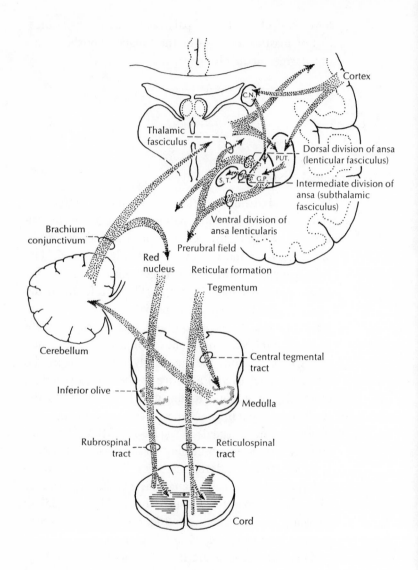

18. Extrapyramidal System

tions are with widely scattered areas. Most of the afferent fibers terminate in the caudate nucleus and putamen, but a few may end in the globus pallidus. Fibers arising from the sensorimotor cortex descend through the internal capsule to terminate in the basal ganglia. All cortical areas, particularly the orbital gyri, give rise to corticostriatal fibers. Nuclei of the thalamus (medial, lateral, ventral, and centromedian) give rise to thalamostriatal fibers, which penetrate the internal capsule to terminate primarily in the putamen. The putamen receives a strong projection from the substantia nigra. Nigrostriatal fibers ascend through the ventral thalamus and penetrate the internal capsule and globus pallidus to end in the putamen.

There are numerous interconnections between the nuclei of the basal ganglia. The efferent projections, however, arise mainly from the globus pallidus. Fibers leave the globus pallidus in three streams. One group of fibers penetrates the internal capsule and forms a compact bundle on the dorsal border of the subthalamic nucleus. This is the dorsal division of the ansa lenticularis or lenticular fasciculus. Arising from this tract is the thalamic fasciculus, which turns laterally and dorsal to the lenticular fasciculus to enter the anterior and lateral divisions of the ventral nucleus of the thalamus. Between the thalamic fasciculus and the dorsal division of the ansa lenticularis is located a nucleus, the zona incerta. Some fibers of the ansa terminate here; others turn ventral to end in the hypothalamus. The remaining fibers of the dorsal division of the ansa lenticularis continue caudally, to terminate in the pretectal region, tegmental and reticular nuclei, and the red nucleus.

A second group of fibers from the globus pallidus penetrates the internal capsule and ends in the subthalamic nucleus. This is the intermediate division of the ansa lenticularis or subthalamic fasciculus. The third group is the ventral division of the ansa lenticularis. It is a compact bundle of fibers ventral to the globus pallidus. It loops around the anterior limb of the internal capsule. Most of these fibers terminate in the prerubral field. This is a nuclear group capping the cephalic pole of the red nucleus.

From the subthalamic nucleus, red nucleus, substantia nigra, and pretectal region, further connections are made with the tegmental and reticular nuclei. The reticulobulbar and reticulospinal tracts descend to end in neurons adjacent to the motor nuclei of cranial nerves and the intermediate gray of the spinal cord. These cells project to the adjacent lower motor neurons. Other descending tracts are the medial longitudinal fasciculus carrying fibers arising from the pretectal region and the rubrospinal and rubrobulbar tracts.

Arising from the tegmental, reticular, and probably other extrapyramidal nuclei, is the central tegmental fasciculus. This tract descends through the central portion of the brain stem to terminate in the inferior olivary nucleus, which projects to the contralateral cerebellar cortex. This brings the extrapyramidal system in relation to the cerebellum. A feedback exists between the basal ganglia and cerebellum since the brachium conjunctivum ends in part in the dorsal thalamus which projects to the putamen. Similarly, there is a feedback circuit between motor cortex and basal ganglia, since the lateral ventral and anterior ventral nuclei of the thalamus send fibers to the precentral gyrus and premotor area.

The extrapyramidal system is concerned with coarse stereotyped movements. It has its principal influence over the proximal musculature. Even following pyramidal tract destruction the individual may be able to carry out numerous motor acts, such as walking and eating, due to the activity of the intact extrapyramidal system. This system is responsible for the associated movements that support voluntary activities, i.e. swinging the arms while walking, changes of facial expression while talking. It also plays an important role in the maintenence of proper muscle tone and postural adjustments.

A somatic motor area can be recognized in the base of the telencephalon of submammalian aquatic forms. It is poorly developed, since in these animals the midbrain tectum is a more important motor integration center. The cells of the somatic area, referred to as the paleostriatum, resemble those of the globus pallidus with which it is homologous. Fibers from this area pass directly back to the dorsal and ventral portions of the thalamus and midbrain tegmentum. These fibers form the lateral forebrain bundle which is homologous to the three divisions of the ansa lenticularis. In mammals the lateral forebrain bundle is broken up into the three divisions of the ansa by the intervening internal capsule which is related to the acquisition of the neocortex. The somatic area receives fibers from the dorsal and ventral portions of the thalamus and from brain-stem reticular formation. A neostriatum appears in amphibians. This is the homologue of the putamen and caudate nucleus. The efferent and afferent connections are basically the same in amphibians, reptiles, birds, and mammals, but as the phylogenetic scale is ascended certain nuclei differentiate out of the tegmentum and reticular formation, i.e. red nucleus, substantia nigra, inferior olivary nucleus, etc. Furthermore, in mammals, connections are made with the neocortex. In birds and reptiles, in addition to a paleostriatum and neostriatum, the basal ganglia contain a hyperstriatum which is the area controlling instinctive behavior in these forms. This structure does not appear to have a homologue in mammals.

Lesions of the basal ganglia or tracts, or other nuclei belonging to the extrapyramidal system, cause altered muscle tone, the loss of associated movements, and the appearance of an adventitial movement. The muscle tone is usually increased, resulting in rigidity. The individual presents a masked expression and except for the adventitial movement there is a paucity of movement. The adventitial movement, which disappears during sleep, may take several forms: there may be rhythmic tremors, slow writhing athetoid movements, or fast jerky choreiform movements.

16

The Reticular Formation

The reticular formation is a diffuse system of nuclei and tracts occupying the central core of the neuraxis from the thalamus to the spinal cord. Phylogenetically, it is the oldest part of the chordate central nervous system. In lower forms it acts as the sole integrator of sensorimotor activity. As the brain increases in complexity, long ascending and descending tracts and associated nuclei appear to develop from the reticular core and assume a peripheral position in the brain stem and spinal cord. In lower forms, most of the ascending tracts terminate in the reticular formation. They attain the thalamus directly only in mammals, but there still remain rich connections of these systems in the reticular formation. Furthermore, a direct corticospinal system can be recognized only in mammals, but even in this group it is poorly developed except in primates. This system also maintains strong corticoreticular connections in mammals, and it is thus apparent that the reticular formation must serve as an important integrator of central nervous system activity.

The cell bodies of the neurons that make up the reticular formation are segmentally arranged in transverse planes; the dendrites branch profusely adjacent to the cell body, whereas the axon usually bifurcates. The ascending limb may ascend as far as the diencephalon, where it terminates in two general areas, i.e. the hypothalamus and the intralaminar, reticular, and medial thalamic nuclei. It is possible that a few pass directly to the basal ganglia. The descending fibers end on cells around the motor nuclei of cranial nerves and intermediate gray of the spinal cord, making up the diffuse reticulobulbar and reticulospinal tracts— in which there is generally recognized a ventral and lateral tract descending diffusely in the corresponding funiculi of the spinal cord. Crossed and uncrossed fibers are present in both the ascending and descending systems. Throughout the course of these axons numerous collaterals are given off at all levels. These branch profusely and terminate in relation to other reticular neurons as well as in all other nuclei of the brain stem, thus it appears that pathways through the reticular formation are both direct and diffuse.

All ascending and descending tracts send numerous collaterals into all levels of the reticular formation. These terminate in relation to the dendrites and cell bodies of the reticular neurons. By this means all sensory modalities reach the reticular formation as do influences from neocortex, limbic lobe, basal ganglia, hypothalamus, thalamus, cerebellum, etc.

It is apparent from the discussion above of the morphology of the reticular formation that it is, either directly or indirectly, in two-way communication with every other area of the central nervous system, this anatomical arrangement is ideal for the reticular formation to perform its most important function of integration.

Although a great deal remains to be determined about the functions of the reticular formation, on the basis of stimulation and ablation experiments and clinical findings it appears that the reticular core exerts an influence over the entire nervous system and in turn has its activity regulated by these same structures. In general, this two-way control takes the form of inhibition and facilitation.

Reticular influences on other areas of the nervous system may conveniently be discussed under the headings "ascending" and "descending." Stimulation of the reticular core induces arousal in the sleeping animal. The electroencephalographic record in such an experiment abruptly changes from the typical sleeping pattern (slow, high amplitude, regular waves) to that of wakefulness (fast, low amplitude, asynchronous waves). This behavioral response recorded by the electroencephalograph indicates an excitatory influence of the reticular formation on the cortex. Stimulation of afferent systems, particularly somatic and auditory, has the same effect. It has been demonstrated that the effect of sensory stimulation is mediated through the reticular formation by way of collaterals from the direct sensory pathways. These pathways may be sectioned below the thalamus without interfering with the response.

Bilateral lesions of the reticular system induce permanent coma even though the direct sensory pathways remain intact. Temporary blockage of the reticular activating system may be brought about by using various anesthetics. Conversely, excitant drugs, such as epinephrine, have a stimulating effect. Furthermore, there is fragmentary, although conflicting, evidence that tranquilizers may exert their influence through the reticular core.

Descending reticular influences are expressed via the neuromuscular system, sensory receptor and conduction systems, and autonomic effectors. Stimulation of the medullary reticular substance inhibits reflex and cortically induced movements, whereas facilitation is observed upon stimulating the pontomesencephalic tegmentum. Normally the activity of these two centers are in perfect balance, allowing for smooth integration of muscular activity. In order to carry out its motor functions the reticular formation must receive signals from a variety of other centers such as vestibular, cerebellar, pallidal, and cortical.

Facilitatory and inhibitory effects on receptors and sensory conduction pathways have been elicited through stimulation of the reticular formation. The influence on receptors is probably mediated through centrifugal fibers to cutaneous receptors, muscle spindles, cochlea, retina, and olfactory bulb. The centrifugal fibers probably have the effect of altering the threshold of the receptors. Reticular stimulation also inhibits or facilitates synaptic transmission at the relay nuclei of the sensory conduction pathways. These phenomena allow the individual to screen the host of stimuli, to accept some and reject others.

It has long been recognized that stimulation or ablation of various areas of the reticular formation has an effect on respiration, circulation, temperature regulation, metabolism, and gastrointestinal motility. These autonomic "centers" are poorly localized and are no doubt intimately related with other functions of the reticular formation.

17

Autonomic Nervous System

The autonomic nervous system (general visceral efferent) innervates smooth muscle, cardiac muscle, and glands. Fibers supplying skeletal muscles arise from cell bodies within the central nervous system and pass directly to the motor end plates. In the autonomic nervous system a neuron within the central nervous system gives rise to a fiber which ends on a multipolar cell in a peripheral ganglion. The axon of this neuron passes to smooth and cardiac muscles and glands and ends as a naked terminal. Two neurons are involved: the cell bodies of the preganglionic are located within the central nervous system; and the cell bodies of the postganglionic are in the ganglion.

The autonomic nervous system has two divisions: the sympathetic and the parasympathetic. In the sympathetic division the preganglionics arise from the thoracic and upper lumbar cord (thoracolumbar outflow). The preganglionics of the parasympathetic division take origin from the brain or sacral cord (craniosacral outflow). Most visceral organs have a dual innervation. The exceptions are the blood vessels, arrector pili muscles, and sweat glands.

The preganglionic fibers of the sympathetic system arise from the intermediolateral cell column in the thoracic and upper lumbar cord. They exit with the ventral root. After passing through the intervertebral foramen they leave the spinal nerve in the communicating ramus to enter a chain of ganglia located adjacent to the vertebral bodies. This is the sympathetic trunk, which extends from the base of the occiput to the coccyx. Some of the fibers terminate in these ganglia either at the level they enter or at some distant point after ascending or descending in the trunk. Postganglionics arising from the ganglia of the trunk join all spinal nerves by way of the communicating ramus. These are distributed to blood vessels, arrector pili muscles, and sweat glands of the periphery. Other preganglionics course through the sympathetic trunk to form the splanchnic nerves. These nerves penetrate the diaphragm and end in ganglia located at the origins of the unpaired branches of the aorta. These are the prevertebral ganglia and consist of the coeliac, superior mesenteric, and inferior mesenteric. Postganglionics reach the viscera by following the blood vessels. Postganglionic sympathetics to the head arise from the highest ganglion of the sympathetic trunk, the superior cervical sympathetic ganglion. They join the internal carotid artery and reach the effectors in the head largely by following blood vessels.

Four cranial nerves contain preganglionic parasympathetics: oculomotor, facial, glossopharyngeal, and vagus. Those in the oculomotor nerve arise from the Edinger-Westphal nucleus in the midbrain, enter the orbit, and terminate in the ciliary ganglion. Postganglionics supply the ciliary muscles and the constrictor of the pupil. Preganglionics of the facial nerve arise from the superior salivatory nucleus of the lower pons and terminate in the pterygopalatine and submandibular ganglia. From the submandibular ganglia, postganglionics supply the submandibular and sublingual glands. The pterygopalatine ganglion gives rise to postganglionics which enter the lacrimal gland. The inferior salivatory nucleus of the upper medulla gives rise to preganglionics which course with the glossopharyngeal nerve. They terminate in the otic ganglion, from which postganglionics supply the parotid gland.

The vagus nerve is the most important parasympathetic nerve. Its preganglionics arise from the dorsal motor nucleus of the vagus in the medulla and course with the vagus into the thorax and abdomen. The ganglia are located adjacent to or in the visceral organ and are very frequently named after that organ, thus there are cardiac, pulmonary, and enteric (in the wall of the gut) ganglia. Postganglionics are short and end on the adjacent cardiac and smooth muscle. The viscera of the pelvis receive parasympathetics from the sacral outflow. Scattered cells within the intermediate gray of sacral segments two through four give rise to preganglionics which exit with the ventral root. They branch from these nerves, forming the nervus erigens, which enters the pelvis. The ganglia are located adjacent to the corresponding organ and the postganglionics supply the smooth muscles of these organs.

The autonomic nervous system has representation in the central nervous system. The most important center for the integration of basic vegetative functions is the hypothalamus (Fig. 19). This is the ventral division of the diencephalon. The hypothalamus contains numerous nuclei, most of which have ill-defined boundaries. Since specific functions are not generally assigned to specific nuclei the hypothalamus is divided into areas: the supraoptic area is the most anterior and is related to the optic chiasma; the tuberal or middle portion is associated with the tuber cinereum; the posterior or mammillary area is related to the mammillary bodies. The hypothalamus may be further divided into medial and lateral areas by the fornix. Related to the hypothalamus both anatomically and functionally is the preoptic area of the telecephalon, which is immediately anterior to the hypothalamus.

The medial forebrain bundle is one of the most important tracts of the hypothalamus. It contains ascending and descending fibers interconnecting the hypothalamus cephalically with olfactory and limbic areas and caudally with the tegmentum. The fornix arises from the hippocampus, and parallels the temporal

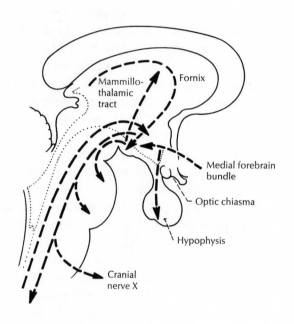

Mammillo-
thalamic
tract

Fornix

Medial forebrain
bundle

Optic chiasma

Hypophysis

Cranial
nerve X

19. Connections of the Hypothalamus

horn and body of the ventricle. Upon reaching the anterior commissure it divides into a precommissural portion, which ends in the preoptic and supraoptic areas, and a postcommissural division, which courses through the hypothalamus to end in the mammillary bodies.

The mammillary peduncle arises from the tegmentum and ascends to terminate in the mammillary bodies and adjacent hypothalamic areas. It also contains some descending fibers. The amygdala projects to the preoptic area and anterior hypothalamus by way of the stria terminalis. Pallidohypothalamic fibers were described in Chapter 15. Finally, the dorsal thalamus, particularly the midline and medial nuclei, sends fibers into the hypothalamus by way of the periventricular system.

A prominent efferent projection of the hypothalamus is the mammillothalamic tract. This tract arises from the mammillary body and terminates in the anterior nucleus of the thalamus, which has extensive connections with the limbic lobe. The supraoptico-hypophyseal tract arises from the supraoptic and paraventricular nuclei, courses through the infundibulum, and ends in the neural lobe. Descending fibers follow two general routes. One group courses diffusely through the reticular formation to reach lower medullary levels. The second descends in the periventricular gray. This includes a discrete bundle, the dorsal longitudinal fasciculus.

As stated previously the hypothalamus is an important integration center of basic vegetative functions which relate to the maintenance of the individual and the species. In order to perform these functions the hypothalamus must receive information from many areas. Afferents from visceral and somatic receptors reach it by way of ascending fibers systems in the reticular formation. Olfaction enters through the medial forebrain bundle. The hypothalamus is intimately related by way of the medial forebrain bundle, fornix, and mammillothalamic tract, to the limbic lobe, which is concerned with emotional tone. Connections with the neocortex are indirect by way of the dorsal thalamus. Finally, certain cells of the hypothalamus are sensitive to the level of circulating hormones.

The hypothalamus utilizes both neural and humoral pathways to reach visceral and somatic effectors and endocrine glands. Descending pathways through the reticular formation and reticulospinal tracts ultimately reach somatic and visceral lower motor neurons. The neurons of the supraoptic and paraventricular nuclei are neurosecretory. They secrete a hormone which passes down the supraoptico-hypophyseal tract to the neural lobe of the hypophysis. This antidiuretic hormone, which regulates the resorption of water by the renal tubules, is stored in the neural lobe to be released at the appropriate time. Neurons in the median eminence of the tuberal region secrete a substance into the hypophyseal portal system which is continuous with the sinuses of the adenohypophysis. The adenohypophysis exerts a marked influence over other endocrine glands via its trophic hormones. By this route the hypothalamus plays an important role in such processes as reproduction and metabolism.

Localization of specific functions within the hypothalamus is difficult. The anterior hypothalamus, however, discharges principally through parasympathetic pathways, whereas stimulation of the posterior regions results in sympathetic responses. The hypothalamus plays a role in temperature regulation: stimulation of the anterior portion produces sweating and vasodilation, and causes heat loss. Other areas of the anterior hypothalamus are concerned with heat production. The hypothalamus is also related to the ascending reticular activating system. Lesions dorsolateral to the mammillary bodies result in somnolence.

Parts of the hypothalamus are concerned with food and water intake. Experiments would indicate that the more medial areas contain a satiety center, whereas feeding behavior is related to the lateral portions.

Emotional behavior is a function of a variety of areas of the central nervous system. The limbic lobe is concerned with emotional tone but, as pointed out above, it has rich connections with the hypothalamus. Lesions in the hypothalamus produce irritability and rage. The hypothalamus is the integrator of the effectory mechanisms in emotional expression.

Other areas of the central nervous system will when stimulated give rise to autonomic responses. Stimulation of the cortex, particularly the limbic lobe, produces autonomic responses. These are related to emotional expression and are mediated through the hypothalamus. The brain-stem reticular formation contains centers that regulate the automatic activity of the respiratory and circulatory systems. Their rhythmic activity may be altered by external and internal stimuli and higher centers such as the hypothalamus.

Since the autonomic nervous system is concerned with basic functions it is present in all vertebrates. The only differences in the periphery in lower forms are that the preganglionics exit by way of the dorsal roots and the ganglia are widely scattered, e.g. the sympathetic chains are not present in aquatic forms. The hypothalamus is present throughout the vertebrates. The only change involves a greater degree of organization of nuclei and fiber connections.

Depending upon the location, lesions of the hypothalamus may result in a variety of signs and symptoms. These are a result of hypothalamic dysfunction and may be expressed as obesity, somnolence, diabetes insipidus, personality change, difficulty in maintaining body temperature, genital dystrophy, sexual precocity, etc.

18

Olfactory and Limbic Systems

The olfactory and limbic systems are discussed together since they are closely related structurally and phylogenetically. Bipolar sensory cells are located in the olfactory membrane in the roof of the nasal cavity (Fig. 20). The peripheral process extends to the surface. Hair-like processes project from the ends of the peripheral fibers. The central processes form the olfactory nerves, which pass through the openings in the cribriform plate to enter the cranial cavity. Resting on the cribriform plate is the olfactory bulb. Within the bulb are large neurons called mitral cells. Several fibers of the olfactory nerves synapse with a dendrite of a mitral cell, forming a glomerulus. The

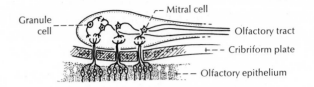

Granule
cell ---

--- Mitral cell

--- Olfactory tract

--- Cribriform plate

--- Olfactory epithelium

A. DETAIL OF OLFACTORY BULB

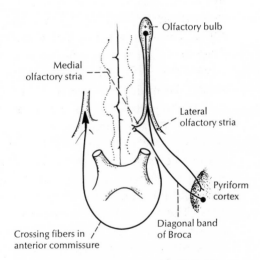

- Olfactory bulb

Medial
olfactory stria ---

Lateral
olfactory stria

Pyriform
cortex

Diagonal band
of Broca

Crossing fibers in
anterior commissure

B. UNDERSIDE OF BRAIN, SHOWING
OLFACTORY CONNECTIONS

20. Olfactory Bulb and Secondary Olfactory Connections

axons of the mitral cells pass back to form the olfactory tract. In their course through the bulb they give off collaterals which end on small granule cells. These project back to the glomerulus, forming a reinforcing circuit.

The olfactory tract passes back to the anterior perforated substance. In the base of the tract are located scattered cells which constitute the anterior olfactory nucleus. Some fibers of the olfactory tract terminate here. The anterior olfactory nucleus sends fibers into the olfactory tract. At the border of the anterior perforated substance the olfactory tract divides into medial and lateral olfactory striae. A few fibers of the tract terminate among cells of the anterior perforated substance. This area, which is highly developed in macrosmatic animals, forms the olfactory tubercle.

Associated with each stria is a thin band of gray matter, the medial and lateral olfactory gyri. The lateral olfactory stria courses along the border of the anterior perforated substance, and at the inferior border of the insula it turns back to enter the temporal lobe. Its fibers terminate in the lateral olfactory gyrus, periamygdaloid area, a portion of the amygdaloid nucleus, and the rostral portion of the parahippocampal gyrus. These constitute the primary olfactory cortex and are known as the pyriform lobe. The lateral olfactory gyrus is frequently referred to as the prepyriform area and the remainder of the pyriform lobe as the entorhinal cortex. This includes the uncus, which is a hook-like rostral end of the parahippocampal gyrus covering the amygdala.

Some fibers of the medial olfactory stria cross in the anterior commissure and terminate in the opposite anterior olfactory nucleus and olfactory bulb, forming another reinforcing circuit. The remaining fibers of the medial olfactory stria enter the medial side of the hemisphere and end in the parolfactory area, septum pellucidum, and subcallosal gyrus (paraterminal gyrus). These constitute what is known as the septal area. The subcallosal gyrus, a thin band of gray matter applied to the underside of the rostrum of the corpus callosum, is separated from the parolfactory area by the posterior parolfactory sulcus. The anterior parolfactory sulcus separates the parolfactory gyrus from the remainder of the medial portion of the hemisphere.

There are three prominent discharge pathways from the olfactory areas cited above to lower centers which may be involved in mediating olfactory reflexes. These same pathways, however, arise in part from regions of the limbic system. The stria terminalis takes origin from the amygdala and follows the medial border of the caudate nucleus to end in the preoptic area and anterior hypothalamus. These areas discharge caudally, as outlined in Chapter 17.

The stria medullaris thalami arises from the septal area, septal nuclei (immediately deep to the septal cortex), and pyriform lobe. It arches over the medial nucleus of the thalamus to end in the habenular nucleus of the epithalamus. Some fibers cross in the habenular commissure to reach the opposite habenular nucleus. The habenulopeduncular tract (fasciculus-retroflexus) relays olfactory impulses to the interpeduncular nucleus of the midbrain. This nucleus, located in the roof of the interpeduncular fossa projects to the tegmental nuclei, which contribute fibers to the dorsal longitudinal fasciculus. Impulses may reach brain-stem nuclei via this tract.

The medial forebrain bundle takes origin from the septal areas and anterior perforated substance and passes back to the preoptic area, hypothalamus, and midbrain tegmentum; these areas project caudally to various brain-stem nuclei. The medial forebrain bundle also contains ascending fibers arising from the areas cited above and ending in olfactory and limbic regions.

The limbic lobe consists of a number of gyri on the medial surface of the hemisphere encircling the brain stem (Fig. 21). Included within this system are the gyrus cinguli located above the corpus callosum; the parahippocampal gyrus in the medial portion of the temporal lobe; the hippocampus and dentate gyrus, which bulge into the temporal horn of the ventricle; and the hippocampal rudiments (induseum griseum), which extend over the corpus callosum and septal area. Since a number of cortical areas and subcortical nuclei are functionally related to the limbic lobe, the concept of a limbic system has been introduced. The limbic system includes, in addition to the structures named above, portions of the orbital gyri, insula, septal nuclei, amygdala, preoptic area, hypothalamus, anterior thalamic nucleus, epithalamus, and midbrain tegmentum.

Certain projection pathways relating to the limbic system, namely, stria medullaris thalami, medial forebrain bundle, and stria terminalis, have already been discussed. Other important tracts are the fornix, mammillothalamic tract, anterior commissure, and cingulum. The fimbria of the fornix arises from the hip-

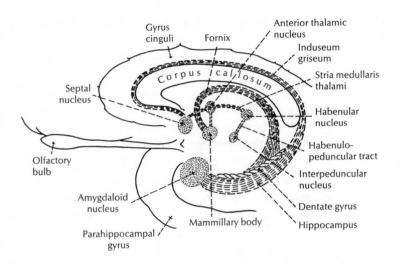

Gyrus cinguli
Fornix
Anterior thalamic nucleus
Induseum griseum
Corpus callosum
Stria medullaris thalami
Septal nucleus
Habenular nucleus
Habenulo-peduncular tract
Olfactory bulb
Interpeduncular nucleus
Amygdaloid nucleus
Dentate gyrus
Hippocampus
Parahippocampal gyrus
Mammillary body

21. Limbic System

pocampus and is attached to the entire length of the hippocampus. At the caudal end of the hippocampus it forms the fornix, which passes into the body of the ventricle; some of the fibers join the opposite fornix. Upon reaching the anterior commissure a smaller precommissural component ends in the septal nuclei, preoptic area, and anterior hypothalamic regions. The larger postcommissural component enters the hypothalamus and terminates in the mammillary body. Some fibers arising from the septal nuclei pass back in the fornix to end in the hippocampus. The mammillothalamic tract passes to the anterior nucleus of the thalamus, which projects to the cortex of the gyrus cinguli.

The anterior commissure is a compact bundle of fibers crossing the midline in the lamina terminalis. The smaller anterior division is olfactory and interconnects the olfactory bulbs and anterior olfactory nucleus. The posterior division interconnects the prepyriform areas, parahippocampal gyri, and neocortex of the temporal lobe.

The cingulum is an important association bundle of the limbic system. It extends from the septal areas back over the corpus callosum, where it forms the white matter of the gyrus cinguli. It turns around the splenium of the corpus callosum to enter the parahippocampal gyrus, and interrelates the septal areas, gyrus cinguli, and parahippocampal gyrus.

All parts of the limbic system are intimately connected with each other, and the system has strong reciprocal connections with the adjacent neocortex. Other afferent projections are from the olfactory areas and the thalamus and hypothalamus. The thalamus and hypothalamus may allow for various somatic and visceral sensory modalities to reach the limbic system.

It is difficult to ascribe any functional localization to specific areas of the limbic system. It appears to regulate emotional tone and influence a wide variety of activities related to emotional tone, such as respiration, cardiac acceleration, chewing and licking motions, various audible sounds such as growling, etc. Stimulation of widely separated points in the limbic system results in these reactions. The common denominator of these responses is that they can be considered as one facet of an emotional expression. The results of lesions support the contention that the limbic system plays a role in regulating emotional tone. Destruction of various areas produce alterations in behavioral mechanisms involved in affective and sexual activities. It appears, therefore, that the limbic lobe is not concerned with the integration of basic homeostatic and adaptive autonomic functions, but rather it modulates functional activities which are integrated at hypothalamic and brain-stem levels.

Although the integration of effectors in rage and fear is possible without a cortex, true emotional expression is dependent upon a neocortical analyzer. The role of the limbic lobe is to modulate or regulate the emotional tone. Somato-autonomic integration takes place largely at the hypothalamic level. The hypothalamus in turn projects to the appropriate somatic, autonomic, and endocrine effectors.

Structures associated with the olfactory and limbic systems are present in all vertebrates. The olfactory nerves, bulb, and secondary olfactory projections to olfactory cortex are found in cyclostomes. The principal phylogenetic change is one of organization and differentiation. A primordial hippocampal and septal area can also be recognized in lower vertebrates. These undergo considerable differentiation in phylogeny. The principal efferent projections of these systems to the epithalamus and hypothalamus is established early. With the development of an extensive neocortex in mammals, olfactory and limbic structures are widely separated and occupy a basal and medial position in the hemisphere.

Clinically the olfactory system is of little importance in man. Anosmia (loss of the sense of smell) may follow frontal fractures that involve the cribriform plate, severing the olfactory nerves. Irritative lesions in the area of the uncus result in olfactory hallucinations known as uncinate fits. Lesions of the limbic system frequently causes behavioral changes. There may be abnormal sexual behavior accompanied by various autonomic changes. Placid behavior follows destruction of the amygdala.

19

Cerebral Cortex

The neocortex is a thin lamina of gray matter on the surface of the hemisphere, averaging about 2.5 mm in thickness. There are approximately 14,000,000,000 cells within the cortex—of the numerous cell types only the principal ones will be discussed. The most common cells are the pyramidal and stellate (Fig. 22). The pyramidal cells vary from small to giant and have an

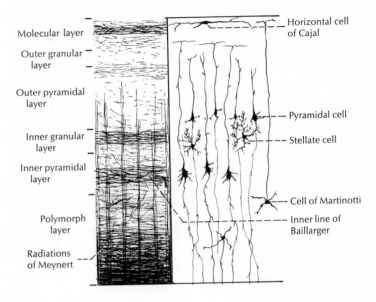

Molecular layer

Outer granular layer

Outer pyramidal layer

Inner granular layer

Inner pyramidal layer

Polymorph layer

Radiations of Meynert

Horizontal cell of Cajal

Pyramidal cell

Stellate cell

Cell of Martinotti

Inner line of Baillarger

After Brodmann (Ranson & Clark)

22. Cerebral Cortex

apical dendrite which extends toward the surface. A basal axon terminates either in the deeper cortical layers or enters the underlying white matter to end in distant cortical areas or subcortical centers. The stellate cell is star-shaped and has numerous short dendrites. The axon, which is short, does not leave the cortex, and is thus associative in function.

Other neurons in the cortex are the horizontal cells of Cajal, polymorph cells, and cells of Martinotti. The horizontal cells of Cajal are found in the most superficial cortical layer. The dendrites and axon are disposed in a horizontal plane—they are associative in function. The polymorph cells vary in shape from spherical to fusiform and are located in the deepest layers. The dendrites extend toward the surface. The axon enters the underlying white matter. The cells of Martinotti are found in all layers. The dendrites are short, and the axon extends toward the surface. They function as association neurons.

On the basis of the distribution of cell types, six cortical layers can be recognized. They are, from superficial to deep: molecular layer, external granular layer, external pyramidal layer, inner granular layer, inner pyramidal layer, and polymorph layer. The molecular layer contains the horizontal cells of Cajal. The principal constituent, however, is the terminations of axons (cells of Martinotti) and dendrites (pyramidal and polymorph cells) of cells in the deeper layers. The principal cell type in the outer granular layer is the small pyramidal cell. Medium-size pyramidal cells dominate the outer pyramidal cell layer. The inner granular layer is composed of stellate cells. Medium, large, and giant pyramidal cells are found in the inner pyramidal layer. Polymorph cells make up the polymorph layer.

In addition to the various cells, certain fiber bands can be recognized in the cortex. The outer line of Baillarger is found within the inner granular layer. It is composed of the terminal ends of afferent fibers, e.g. thalamic radiations. Within the inner pyramidal layer is found the inner line of Baillarger. It is composed of association fibers from other cortical areas. The radiations of Meynert are vertical bundles of fibers formed from axons of pyramidal and polymorph cells entering the white matter.

Although the six cortical layers can be recognized at some stage of development in all areas of the neocortex, they may not be obvious in some regions in the adult. Furthermore there is considerable variation in the development of the various layers. On the basis of pattern of lamination, as many as 250 different areas have been described, and although not conclusively demonstrated in all cases, these variations may reflect functional differences.

The white matter is composed of association, commissural, and projection fibers. The association fibers interconnect cortical areas within one hemisphere. They may be short loops between adjacent gyri or long bundles relating distant points. An example of a short association loop is the stratum calcarinum, which interconnects the cuneus and lingual gyrus. The long association bundles are the cingulum, uncinate fasciculus, superior and inferior longitudinal fasciculi, superior and inferior occipitofrontal fasciculi, and vertical occipital bundle (Fig. 23).

The cingulum was discussed in Chapter 18. The

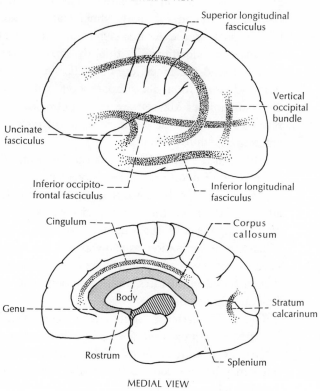

LATERAL VIEW

Superior longitudinal
fasciculus

Vertical
occipital
bundle

Uncinate
fasciculus

Inferior occipito-
frontal fasciculus

Inferior longitudinal
fasciculus

Cingulum

Corpus
callosum

Genu

Body

Stratum
calcarinum

Rostrum

Splenium

MEDIAL VIEW

23. Association Bundles

uncinate fasciculus interconnects the cortices of the basal frontal region and temporal pole. The superior longitudinal fasciculus passes back from the frontal lobe above the insula to the parietal, occipital, and temporal regions. The caudal fibers of this bundle run vertically and constitute the vertical occipital bundle. Deep to the superior longitudinal fasciculus is the inferior occipitofrontal fasciculus. This bundle interconnects frontal, temporal, and occipital areas. The inferior longitudinal fasciculus extends from the temporal to the occipital poles. The superior occipitofrontal fasciculus is found between the caudate nucleus and corpus callosum.

The commissural fibers relate the cortices of the two hemispheres and pass through the corpus callosum, which in the midsagittal plane is divided into splenium, body, genu, and rostrum (Fig. 23). Fibers that course through the splenium turn back toward the occipital poles, forming the major forceps. The minor forceps is formed by fibers interconnecting the frontal poles through the genu. The majority of the fibers relate association areas and are both symmetrically and asymmetrically connected.

The projection fibers relate the cortex with subcortical centers and are both ascending and descending. They traverse the corona radiata and internal capsule. The internal capsule in a transverse plane has the appearance of a shallow V with the apex directed medially (Fig. 24). The frontothalamic fibers course through the lateral portion of the anterior limb and the frontopontine in the medial portion. The corticobulbar component of the pyramidal system is located in the genu and the corticospinal in the anterior portion of the

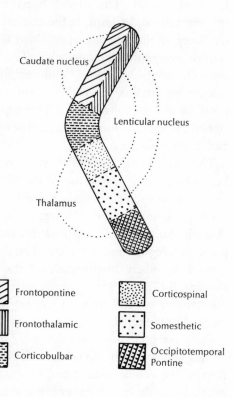

Caudate nucleus

Lenticular nucleus

Thalamus

▨	Frontopontine	▦	Corticospinal
▥	Frontothalamic	⦙	Somesthetic
▤	Corticobulbar	▩	Occipitotemporal Pontine

24. Internal Capsule

posterior limb. The somesthetic thalamic radiations ascend through the middle of the posterior limb. Occipitotemporopontine fibers are found in the posterior portion of the posterior limb. The optic radiations assume a retrolenticular position and the auditory radiations, a sublenticular. Other projection fibers, both ascending and descending, connect the cortex with the thalamus, corpus striatum, reticular formation, red nucleus, and substantia region, and are diffusely scattered in the internal capsule.

Functionally the cortex can be divided into primary and association areas. The primary sensory areas receive the thalamic projections of various sensory pathways. The primary somesthetic cortex is located in the postcentral gyrus (Fig. 25). This gyrus extends from the lateral fissure to the medial side of the hemisphere, where, with the medial portion of the precentral gyrus, it forms the paracentral lobule. Separated from the precentral gyrus by the central sulcus, it is the most anterior gyrus of the parietal lobe and receives the somesthetic radiations from the posteroventral nucleus of the thalamus and projects to association areas. The body is represented somatotopically on the postcentral gyrus. The greater the concentration of receptors in any part of the body the larger the cortical area representing that part. The head area is located adjacent to the lateral fissure, the lower extremity on the medial side of the hemisphere, and the upper extremity intermediate.

The primary visual cortex is located on the medial side of the occipital lobe in the lingual gyrus and cuneus. The optic radiations arising from the lateral geniculate body terminate in the visual cortex. The

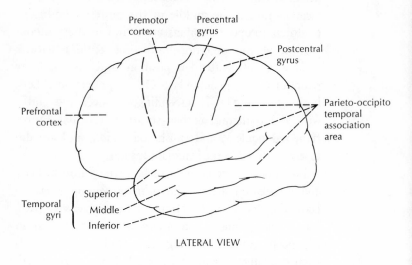

LATERAL VIEW

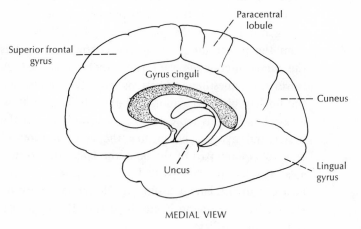

MEDIAL VIEW

25. Cortical Localization

macular area of the retina is represented in the posterior portion and the more peripheral areas of the retina in the anterior part of the visual cortex.

The primary auditory cortex is located in the transverse temporal gyri on the lower bank of the lateral fissure. The auditory radiations from the medial geniculate body project to this area. Tonotopic localization exists in the auditory cortex. High frequencies are represented posteromedially, and low frequencies, anterolaterally.

The primary gustatory and vestibular areas are not as clearly defined as the other sensory areas. Taste seems to be localized in the insula and adjacent parietal lobe. This area receives a strong projection from the posteroventral nucleus of the thalamus. Vestibular sensations can be elicited from stimulation of the superior temporal gyrus. These are, however, poorly localized, and other cortical areas have been implicated.

The precentral gyrus constitutes the primary motor cortex. It is closely related functionally and morphologically with the premotor area. There is a somatotopic localization in the precentral gyrus comparable to that found in the postcentral gyrus. It projects primarily into the pyramidal tract. The premotor area, in addition to contributing to the pyramidal tract, has strong connections with the precentral gyrus. It also sends fibers to various subcortical motor nuclei, e.g. basal ganglia, pontine nuclei, reticular formation, etc.

A supplementary motor area as well as secondary sensory areas have been described. These are located adjacent to the corresponding primary area.

The remainder of the cortex is referred to as association cortex. The portion in front of the premotor area is the prefrontal lobe. This area endows the individual with the ability to plan and look to the future; to be persistent in solving a problem; to control his emotions; to deal sociably with others; and to face up to a problem and relate it to past, present, and future experiences.

Patients with lesions of the prefrontal lobes are easily distracted, unable to plan, tactless, extroverted, and without emotional tensions. There may be no loss of basic intelligence, but the ability to abstract is lessened. Prefrontal lobotomies, which involve sectioning the connections of the prefrontal lobes with the rest of the brain, have been performed on psychotic patients and for the relief of intractable pain. Many mentally ill patients have been helped by this procedure, which does not eliminate pain, but rather the patient's anxieties toward pain, and thus he becomes indifferent to it.

The posterior parietal, lateral occipital, and posterior temporal cortices constitute a large association area. It may be referred to as a gnostic center. It is concerned with motor speech and understanding the spoken and written word and the appreciation of symbolism. Portions of the temporal lobe in conjunction with subcortical centers play a role in memory.

Lesions in the parietal, occipital, and temporal areas, particularly on the dominant side may cause apraxia, aphasia, and agnosia. Apraxia is the inability to perform complex motor acts. There is no paralysis or other motor impairment and automatic and associated movements are normal. Aphasia is the loss of ability to use signs and symbols in communication. Expressive aphasia is the inability to express one's thoughts either by speaking or writing. Receptive aphasia is the inability to appreciate the spoken or written word. Agnosia is the inability to recognize and interpret what is felt, seen, or heard.

The beginnings of the neocortex may appear in reptiles and birds, but it is usually considered a mammalian structure. In subprimates most of the cortex is devoted to primary sensory and motor areas. These are at first poorly organized with little topographical localization. In higher forms there is a progressive increase in the organization of the primary areas. In primates, particularly man, large association areas develop in the prefrontal, parietal, occipital, and temporal zones. As already stated, these areas are concerned with higher intellectual functions.

20

Meninges and Cerebrospinal Fluid

The brain and spinal cord are separated from the bony walls of the cranium and vertebral canal by three fibrous membranes, collectively called the meninges. They are named, from without inwards, the dura mater, arachnoid mater, and pia mater (Fig. 26). The dura mater or pachymenix is a strong non-elastic membrane usually described as consisting of two layers: external endosteal and internal meningeal. The outer endosteal layer everywhere tightly adheres to the inner surface of the cranial vault and is continuous with

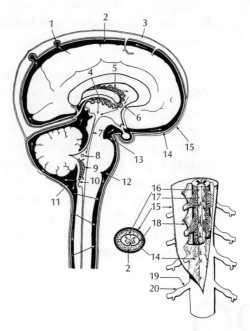

1	arachnoid villi	11	cisterna magna
2	subarachnoid space	12	pontine cistern
3	superior sagittal sinus	13	interpeduncular cistern
4	choroid plexus of the third ventricle	14	arachnoid mater
5	choroid plexus of the lateral ventricle	15	dura mater
6	interventricular foramen	16	pia mater
7	cerebral aqueduct	17	dorsal root
8	lateral foramen of Luschka	18	dentate ligament
9	choroid plexus of the fourth ventricle	19	spinal nerve
10	medial foramen of Magendie	20	dorsal root ganglion

26. Meninges and Cerebrospinal Fluid

the pericranium at the foramen magnum and cranial nerve foramina. The meningeal layer follows the inner contours of the skull and is tightly joined to the endosteal layer except at the sites of the venous sinuses and where it is reflected inwards to form partitions between various portions of the brain. These fibrous projections are called the falx cerebri, tentorium cerebelli, falx cerebelli, and diaphragma sellae (Fig. 27). The sickle-shaped falx cerebri is attached to the entire length of the calvaria at its midline and extends inward into the longitudinal fissure to form a fibrous septum between the cerebral hemispheres. Its rostral apex is securely attached to the crista galli of the sphenoid bone, while the dorsal attached border continues backward to terminate on the internal occipital protuberance. Located within the dorsal attached border of the falx cerebri is the endothelial-lined superior sagittal sinus. The ventral or concave border forms a free edge which is closely associated with the dorsal surface of the corpus callosum. Directly behind the splenium of the corpus callosum it fuses along the dorsal midline surface of the horizontally placed tentorium cerebelli. Rostrally, the free edge of the falx cerebri contains the inferior sagittal sinus. This sinus continues backward to join the straight sinus located in the attached borders of the falx cerebri and tentorium cerebelli. The tentorium cerebelli forms a roof over the posterior cranial fossa and thereby separates the dorsal surface of the cerebellum from the occipital lobes of the cerebral hemispheres. Its internal border is free and deeply concave and, together with the dorsum sellae, form the tentorial notch, which is occupied by the midbrain. The outer circumferential border is attached to the occipital

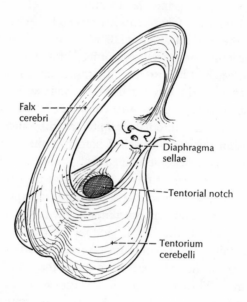

Falx
cerebri

Diaphragma
sellae

Tentorial notch

Tentorium
cerebelli

27. Reflections of the Dura Mater

bone along a groove which contains the transverse or lateral venous sinus and along the lips of a groove on the dorsal aspect of the petrous temporal bone which affords passage for the superior petrosal sinus. Continuing forward, the tentorium cerebelli attaches itself to the posterior clinoid process. The diaphragma sellae is a quadrangular portion of the meningeal dura which roofs over the hypophyseal fossa except for a small central aperture that allows for the passage of the infundibular process. Its outer attached border contains the circular venous sinus. The falx cerebelli is a small triangular reflection of the meningeal layer of dura mater situated directly below the internal occipital proturberance. The outer border is anchored along the midline of the occipital bone and contains the occipital sinus. The free border of the falx cerebelli projects inwardly a short distance between the cerebellar hemispheres.

The inner meningeal layer continues as a tubular extension through the foramen magnum to invest loosely the spinal cord. While the cord ends at the upper part of the second lumbar vertebra the dural tube continues caudally to terminate in a cul-de-sac at the second sacral vertebra. It loosely invests the spinal cord; unlike the cranial dura, a space is found between the meningeal layer and the outer periosteal layer. This space is called the extradural space and is filled with a meshwork of areolar tissue and fat. It also contains blood vessals associated with the walls and contents of the vertebral canal.

The arachnoid and pia mater are usually described as two membranes united by trabeculae of connective tissue in the meshes of which is formed the fluid-filled subarachnoid or cerebrospinal fluid (C.S.F.) space. Because of the trabecular connections of the arachnoid and pia the two membranes are referred to as the leptomeninges. The arachnoid mater, as the name implies, is a delicate web-like membrane lying deep to the meningeal layer of dura mater in the cranioverte-bral cavities, but separated from this layer by a potential subdural space. The pia mater, on the other hand, closely invests the surface of the brain and spinal cord. This close attachment is made possible by means of connective tissue projections called the pial-glial membrane. Blood vessels supplying the central nervous system ramify in this layer, and as these vessels pierce the nervous system they carry a cone-like reflection of the pia mater. The cleft thus formed between the two layers of pia is called the perivascular space and extends only a short distance into the substance of the brain. The pial covering of the spinal cord presents a thickened narrow band along the crest of the anterior fissure and is referred to as the linea splendens; laterally the pia extends outwardly as a lateral longitudinal ridge called the ligmentum denticulatum, so called because of the tooth-like processes which extend from its free edge through the arachnoid to terminate on the dura mater. Normally, there are 21 pairs of these projections, extending from the foramen magnum to the termination of the spinal cord. At this level the pia mater continues inferiorly as a slender cord, the filum terminale, which pierces the lower end of the arachnoid and dural tube to fuse with the periosteum on the back of the coccyx. The ligmenta denticula and filum terminale subserve a supporting function for the spinal cord.

Surrounding the exiting spinal and cranial nerves are projections of the meninges. Along the spinal nerves the dura mater ensheathes both the dorsal and ventral roots to fuse with the epineurium adjacent to the distal portion of the dorsal root ganglia. The arachnoid also forms a separate sheath for both roots and terminates near the proximal portion of the dorsal root ganglia while the pia contributes the innermost layer around each nerve root and is prolonged into the intervertebral foramen and blends with the epineurium. The same general arrangement persists for most of the cranial nerves. The optic nerve is an exception since it is in an extension of the central nervous system and is therefore completely surrounded by the three meningeal layers and associated subarachnoid space.

The subarachnoid space is everywhere filled with cerebrospinal fluid, which is clear and colorless and having properties similar to the aqueous humour of the eye. Normally the C.S.F. contains small amounts of protein and glucose, a few lymphocytes, and rather high concentrations of potassium and sodium chloride, which are probably important in keeping C.S.F. in osmotic equilibrium with the blood. The bulk of fluid is formed by specialized structures called the choroid plexuses, which are located in the lateral, third and fourth ventricles of the brain. The choroid plexuses constitute a blood-brain barrier limiting the passage of certain substances, particularly protein and bacteria. This limitation may, however, be modified by disease. Whether or not the ependyma and other neuroglial cells contribute to its formation is not certain. The quantity of the fluid in the adult varies from 80 to 200 cc. Since the C.S.F. is more or less continually formed in the lateral ventricles, it must circulate through the interventricular foramina and, with that produced in the third ventricle, pass through the cerebral aqueduct of the midbrain to the fourth ventricle. Additional fluid is added here from the choroid plexuses of the fourth ventricle and this, coupled with the other fluid, escapes by way of one medial and two lateral foramina located in the roof of the fourth ventricle into the subarachnoid space surrounding the brain and spinal cord. Circulation in the subarachnoid space is considered sluggish and its movement or diffusion is accomplished by pulsations of the choroid plexuses. Another important factor in keeping the fluid moving is the pressure in the capillaries, which at the site of formation is higher than at the site of absorption. Exactly how the cerebrospinal fluid returns to the venous circulation is debatable, but it is generally agreed that a major portion of the fluid gains entrance into the venous system by way of finger-like projections of the arachnoid membrane extending into the lumen of the superior sagittal sinus. Especially large arachnoid granulations (Pacchionian bodies) are also found in lateral extensions of the superior sagittal sinus and may be especially large in older individuals. A small amount of fluid may also reach the venous system in still other ways, such as along the roots of the cerebrospinal nerves or possibly directly from the subarachnoid space.

21

Cerebral Circulation

The brain receives its blood supply from two paired arteries: the internal carotids and vertebrals (Fig. 28). The vertebral arteries pierce the spinal dura and arachnoid in the area between the base of the skull and atlas to enter the cranial cavity through the foramen magnum. At this point they move to the ventral surface of the brain stem and join to form a single vessel, the basilar artery. This vessel continues rostrally, to end by dividing into two posterior cerebral arteries at the superior border of the pons. Paired vessels, the posterior communicating arteries, extend from the posterior cerebrals to join the internal carotids at this level. On reaching the base of the skull the internal carotid arteries enter the carotid canals situated in the petrous portion of the temporal bone to continue upward through the cavernous sinus and emerge within the cranial cavity lateral to the optic chiasma. Anatomically the vertebral and internal carotid arteries are two separate systems which are connected by varying degrees through the posterior and anterior communicating arteries. Thus, the various branches at the base of the brain form a circle, the circle of Willis. There is, however, a considerable amount of variation in this vascular circle in that some of the communicating branches may be absent or vary considerably in size.

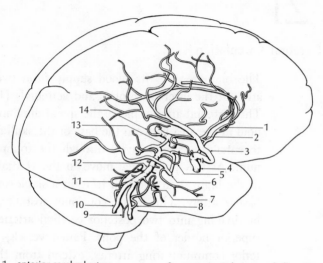

1	anterior cerebral artery	8	posterior inferior cerebellar artery
2	anterior communicating artery	9	anterior spinal artery
3	middle cerebral artery	10	vertebral artery
4	internal carotid artery	11	anterior inferior cerebellar artery
5	superior cerebellar artery	12	basilar artery
6	posterior cerebellar artery	13	posterior communicating artery
7	internal auditory artery	14	anterior choroidal artery

28. Arterial Supply of the Brain

From *Pathology of the Nervous System*, Vol. I, edited by
J. Minckler et al. Copyright © 1967 by McGraw-Hill, Inc.
Used by permission of Mc-Graw Hill Book Company.

Normally the communications between these two arterial systems is extensive enough so that blood flow to the brain is not impaired if one of the major vessels is interrupted.

The posterior inferior cerebellar arteries arise from the vertebral artery shortly after they enter the cranial cavity and pass dorsally, winding around the medulla to the inferior surface of the cerebellum. In their course they supply the dorsal lateral portion of the medulla as well as the inferior surface of the cerebellum. In its course over the pons the basilar artery gives rise to a medial and lateral group of pontine arteries. The medial group penetrates the midline of the pons to supply the pyramidal tract, medial lemniscus, medial longitudinal fasciculus, and the IV, VI, and III cranial nerve nuclei. The lateral group supplies the middle cerebellar peduncle, facial nucleus, and the trigeminal nucleus. The internal auditory artery branches from the caudal portion of the basilar and courses with the VIIIth nerve to supply the internal ear. The anterior inferior cerebellar artery arises from the basilar in the lower half of the pons. It courses dorsally, supplying the middle cerebellar peduncle, some of the vestibular nuclei, and the anterior and inferior portions of the cerebellum. Just before the basilar bifurcates into the posterior cerebrals, the superior cerebellar artery is given off. As it passes the lateral surface of the upper pons it supplies the spinal lemniscus and then enters the cerebellum, supplying its superior surface and most of the deep cerebellar nuclei. The posterior cerebral artery is a terminal branch of the basilar and at its origin gives rise to a number of penetrating branches which supply the medial portion of the thalamus, portion of the choroid plexus, cerebral peduncles, tectum, and internal capsule. It then passes back between the temporal lobe and brain stem to the ventral surface of the temporal lobe, finally branching out on the medial surface of the occipital lobe. Throughout its course it gives cortical branches to the medial and tentorial surfaces of the temporal lobe and the medial and tentorial surfaces of the occipital lobe. The posterior communicating artery, which extends from the posterior cerebral to the internal carotid, gives rise to penetrating arteries which supply portions of the optic chiasma, subthalamic region, basis pedunculi, internal capsule, and thalamus.

The ophthalmic artery arises from the internal carotid immediately after it enters the cranial cavity. It passes through the optic foramen and runs forward and laterally below the optic nerve to enter the orbit. The anterior choroid artery is a small branch which arises near the termination of the internal carotid. This vessel passes posteriorly between the cerebral peduncle and the medial surface of the temporal lobe. It supplies the posterior portion of the choroid plexus of the lateral ventricle and portions of the optic tract and radiations, amygdaloid nucleus, caudate nucleus, basis pedunculi, lenticular nucleus, and anterior commissure.

After giving off the branches named above, each internal carotid artery divides into two principal terminal vessels, the anterior cerebral and middle cerebral. The anterior cerebral artery passes forward and medially over the base of the brain to enter the sagittal fissure. Shortly after these vessels branch off the internal carotid they are interconnected by the anterior communicating artery. Numerous small perforating branches leave the anterior cerebral near its origin and pass through the anterior perforated substance to feed the cephalic portions of the internal capsule and corpus striatum. The main trunk continues forward and dorsally around the genu of the corpus callosum and then posteriorly above the corpus callosum, terminating in the region of the parieto-occipital fissure, where it may anastomose with terminal branches of the posterior cerebral. At this level it supplies the corpus callosum and the medial surface of the frontal and parietal lobes. The anterior and posterior cerebrals usually supply a narrow band of cortex on the dorsal and lateral surfaces of the hemisphere. The anterior cerebral also gives rise to penetrating branches which supply the head of the caudate nucleus, internal capsule, and part of the thalamus. Lenticular striate branches run upward between the lenticular nucleus and external capsule to supply in part these latter structures. The main trunk of the artery continues laterally into the lateral fissure, and exiting through the lateral fissure it branches to supply the cortex of the lateral surface of the frontal, parietal, occipital, and temporal lobes. In its course through the lateral fissure, the middle cerebral supplies the cortex of the insula as well as the opercular surfaces of the frontal, parietal, and temporal lobes (including the transverse temporal gyri). The remaining, and larger, of the two terminal branches of the carotid is the middle cerebral artery. This vessel passes into the lateral fissure and distributes numerous branches along its course to the hemisphere. Small central branches arise near the base of this vessel, the medial and lateral striate arteries, which supply portions of the globus pallidus, internal capsule, and caudate nucleus.

In general it may be stated that anastomoses do not occur between the cortical and penetrating branches of the cerebral arteries. There may or may not be anastomoses between neighboring cortical vessels. In any case they are seldom sufficient to maintain nutrition of the area if one of the vessels is occluded. The central branches of the cortical vessels may occasionally show anastomoses, but these too are rarely adequate.

The spinal cord is supplied by the two posterior spinal arteries and the single ventral spinal artery. The latter arises as two trunks from the vertebral arteries, which anastomose ventrally and descend in the ventral median fissure of the spinal cord. Throughout its extent its flow is augmented by communicating vessels passing through the intervertebral foramen that arise from the systemic circulation. Anterior spinal arteries supply approximately the ventral two-thirds of the spinal cord. The posterior spinal arteries arise from either the vertebral arteries or the posterior inferior cerebellar arteries. They are small, frequently disconnected arteries that descend adjacent to the point of entrance of the dorsal roots. They also communicate with the systemic circulation through each of the intervertebral foramina. Collectively they supply the dorsal one-third of the spinal cord.

The venous outflow of the brain can be arbitrarily divided into a superficial and deep system of veins. The superficial veins essentially drain the cortical and adjacent subcortical areas of the brain while the more deeply placed veins drain the basal ganglia, thalamus, and hypothalamus. The veins associated with the cerebral cortex are divided into inferior and superior system. The superior portion is divided into frontal, precentral, postcentral, and occipital groups, which drain into the superior sagittal sinus (Fig. 29). The ventrolateral surface of the cortex and the inferior surface of the frontal, temporal, and occipital lobes are drained by the inferior cerebral veins. These empty into various sinuses: the superior and inferior petrosal, cavernous, transverse, and sphenoparietal sinuses, and also into the vena magna cerebri.

The deep white matter of the hemispheres, and portions of the basal ganglia, choroid plexusus, dorsal thalamus, and hypothalamus, are drained by the paired internal cerebral veins (veins of Galen). These vessels continue posteriorly from the area of the intraventricular foramen dorsal to the thalamus, where they unite to form the vena magna cerebri. This vascular complex also receives collaterals from the basal vein, which drains portions of the insular region and corpus striatum. Other diencephalic structures are drained by penetrating veins that pass through the perforating substance to empty into the cavernous sinus or basilar plexus. As in the case of other organs of the body, the venous drainage of the brain is subject to considerable variation. This, coupled with extensive anastomotic connections between the deep and superficial groups of veins, affords numerous collateral pathways for venous discharge. Furthermore the intracerebral venous system is also connected with veins of the face and scalp. These interconnecting vessels are called emissary veins and are of some clinical importance in that they do not contain valves and thus may serve as routes for infectious agents to pass from outside the walls of the cranium into the intracranial venous sinuses.

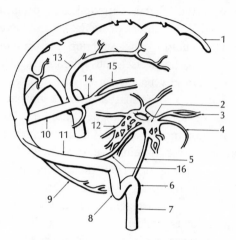

1 superior sagittal sinus	9 occipital sinus
2 cavernous sinus	10 straight sinus
3 ophthalmic veins	11 transverse sinus
4 sphenoparietal sinus	12 basilar venous plexus
5 inferior petrosal sinus	13 inferior sagittal sinus
6 jugular bulb	14 deep cerebral vein
7 internal jugular vein	15 internal cerebral vein
8 sigmoid sinus	16 superior petrosal sinus

29. Venous Drainage of the Brain

From *Pathology of the Nervous System*, Vol. I, edited by J. Minckler et al. Copyright © 1967 by McGraw-Hill, Inc. Used by permission of Mc-Graw Hill Book Company.

The superior sagittal sinus arises from an emissary vein which communicates with veins of the nasal cavity through the foramen caecum. The superior sagittal sinus passes backwards within the dura of the attached margin of the falx cerebri to the confluens sinus. This latter structure is a dilatation found at the junction of the falx cerebri and tentorium cerebelli. It communicates with the superior sagittal sinus, straight sinus, and the paired transverse sinuses. The inferior sagittal sinus courses posteriorly in the free margin of the falx cerebri and in its course drains the corpus callosum and adjacent medial cortical areas. It terminates by joining with the vena magna cerebri, and together they form the straight sinus. This sinus in turn continues posteriorly in the midline of the tentorium cerebelli to empty into the confluens sinus. The superior portion of the cerebellum drains into the straight sinus. The vena magna cerebri is formed by the union of the two internal cerebral veins mentioned above. In its course the vena magna cerebri passes over the pineal body and tectum, receiving additional tributaries from these areas.

A small marginal sinus surrounds the border of the foramen magnum and is drained by the occipital sinuses, which in turn communicate with the internal vertebral plexus and thereby connect the vertebral venus plexus with the intracranial sinuses. The transverse sinuses subserve the function of draining the confluens sinus. They pass laterally to the point where the petrous bone meets the squamous portion of the temporal bone. Here they turn ventrally, passing in a groove at the base of the posterior slope of the petrous bone and thus forming the sigmoid sinus. They terminate by emptying into the jugular bulb which is found within the jugular foramen. Leading from this bulb is the internal jugular vein.

The cavernous sinuses are located one on either side of the sella turcica and are interconnected by the intercavernous sinus situated in the anterior and posterior margins of the diaphragma sellae. In addition the cavernous sinuses receive the venous drainage from the superior and inferior ophthalmic veins and the sphenoparietal sinuses. Some of the penetrating veins arising from the base of the brain and a few of the interior cerebral veins draining the cortex also empty into the cavernous sinuses. The cavernous sinuses drain by way of the superior and inferior petrosal sinuses. Each petrosal sinus extends back over the crest of the petrous portion of the temporal bone to empty into the sigmoid sinus at its junction with the transverse sinus. The inferior petrosal vein passes back in a groove formed by the petro-occipital suture to empty into the jugular bulb. It receives the major venous drainage from the inferior portion of the cerebellum. The basilar plexus, located on the clivus of the skull, has connections with the cavernous sinus and also communicates with the vertebral venous system, a system of veins which extends throughout the length of the spinal canal in the epidural space. These veins drain the contents of the spinal canal and communicate at every intervertebral foramen with the systemic circulation. The spinal cord is drained directly by a single anterior spinal vein which accompanies the artery, and by small discontinuous posterior spinal veins which accompany the comparable arteries. These in turn drain into the vertebral venous system. The vertebral venous system is devoid of valves and has a very low hydrostatic pressure. These points associated with the fact that it communicates with all intervertebral levels with the systemic circulation make the vertebral venous system an ideal pathway for the spread of aberrant metastases and infections.

Index